TIGER
IN THE
SKY

PAT JACKSON

TRULEIGH PRESS

The Extraordinary Story

Of Toon Ghose

Available from

Truleigh Press
The Gables
Upper Station Road
Henfield
West Sussex
BN5 9PL

A CIP catalogue record of this book is available from the British Library.

Printed in Great Britain.

ISBN 1 873475 25 X

Note: Bengali and Hindi - Toon Ghose's own transliteration.

India Pre-1947

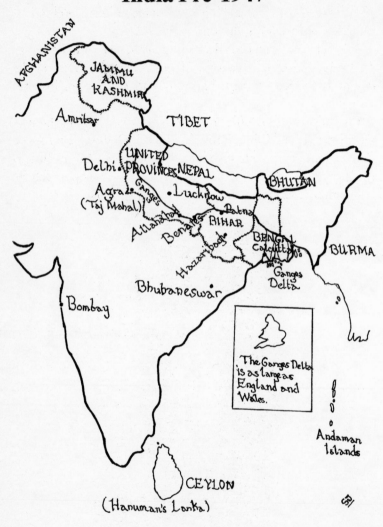

CHAPTER 1

"*Deko*! Look!"

The small boy bounced up and down like a coiled spring among the spectators, jabbing a brown finger into the cloudless blue sky, eyes wild with excitement. "*Deko.*"

The Tiger Moth wheeled and looped above them like a huge bird revelling in its freedom. The exhilarating buzz of the engine throbbed through his body and made even his toes wriggle.

Oh, he would love his father for ever for bringing them to see this wonderful thing. Baba, that amazing father, stood beside him, tall and dark. He glanced up, shyly, then forgot him as the aeroplane flew right above their heads, so low he felt he could almost jump up and touch it.

Toon

His small face was all eyes, huge dark eyes that followed every tiny movement as though some invisible thread linked them to the Tiger Moth, pulled them gently upwards. He stood still now.

He was used to looking up - at Baba, at his beautiful Ma, at his many aunts and uncles, at his elder brother, and even at his baby sister from her perch on Ayah's hips. He was tiny for his age, and that must be why people so far above him often didn't understand what he was trying to say.

No need for words in that aeroplane. He would be absolute king of the sky. And all the people watching on the grassy airfield would be tiny. All the people in Hazaribagh would shrink away, all the people in India disappear. He squirmed in ecstasy.

How he wanted to be up there with that pilot. It would be so impossibly wonderful. Imagine being that man, so splendid in his goggles, his head actually up in the sky.

But what was happening now?

On a pole taller than Baba he could see a large red handkerchief. He held his breath while the Tiger Moth swooped down. Then, unbelievable, pure magic, the red trophy was fluttering on the wing tip and the aeroplane soared into the sky. He didn't know how to contain himself.

"*Odikay deko*! Look at that!" People turned to see who was shouting so wildly, and smiled.

Had it really happened? He jumped up and down, his plimsolls bruising the grass. He waved his arms, he went berserk, he was going to burst.

"*Tumar kee hoachay*, Toon? What's the matter with you?" shrilled Ma.

He calmed down, exhausted, and looked at Ma, so small beside Baba. She was wearing his favourite yellow sari with the red flowers, her shiny black hair hanging loose to her hips. He looked at her face, so beautiful he always wanted to reach up and stroke it, but there was no look of wonder, only a kind of loving impatience. Had she missed it then? Hadn't she seen?

Baba seemed more god-like, more remote than ever in his dhoti and best *punjabi* of cream silk. But it was he who had taken them all to stay in the bungalow and brought them to this wonderful display. So surely he had been watching. Surely he saw the aeroplane pick up the red handkerchief.

Toon searched the dark handsome face so far above him.

"That was very skilful," Baba said, but his eyes did not flash and there was no excitement in his deep voice.

Puzzled, Toon turned to his elder brother. "Dada, *deko*." But Dada stood quietly, still neat in his shirt and shorts, and didn't seem to know what all the fuss was about.

His little sister Sheila on Ayah's hips gurgled and waved her chubby arms at him. He pulled a face at her. If only she could talk ... She squirmed as Ayah tried to wipe her chin with the end of her pink sari. She wasn't their usual ayah because they were on holiday but she had the same dark hair - not as long as Ma's - and the same big red spot below her parting. Her eyes were all for Sheila. Trust her - probably she hadn't even seen what happened.

Only his little brother Habu seemed to share in the excitement, laughing and tumbling round everybody's legs, but he always did that and he wasn't even looking at the sky. When he got just a little bit older, Toon was sure that Habu would be the one to understand these things. He resisted the temptation this time to trip him up.

The aeroplane was higher than the hills behind the airfield now. He looked at the thousands of spectators in their best clothes, some with faces still upturned, some already gathering up their possessions. A few, like his father, were putting their shawls around their shoulders, feeling the heat begin to slide from the winter day. In all those faces there were no sparks of excitement to match his own.

For a moment their indifference fell over him like a chill shadow and the Hazaribagh airfield might have been deserted. He would have to dream alone. There was no-one who could share this with him.

But the chill shadow was only passing over like the aeroplane, like a premonition. Who cared about the others, when he'd felt that magic throb through him. Soon he was jumping and shouting again.

"Ma, when can we see another aeroplane?"

"Oh, I don't know, Toon." Ma laughed.

Some feelings are too deep to be expressed in words. They are rooted far down in the soul in a space where language as we know it has not been invented. Words do not count.

Such feelings are a knowing which defies logic, an affinity, an infinity, an already there. They are naked and cannot be clothed.

Do they come from another place, or another life of which one is an unconscious reincarnation? Or are they too personal, too much a part of every cell to have a separate existence? Perhaps they can only be vaguely recognized in a tiger's eye or in the blueness of the sky. Or perhaps the only way to catch a glimpse of them is to watch their effect on a life.

Six-year-old Toon did not worry himself about such questions but his whole body understood that one day he would have to get up in that unfathomable sky - it was where he belonged. One day he was going to fly.

As Ma drew her sari across her face and they followed Baba out of the airfield, he kept looking over his shoulder, reluctant to leave such a fantastic place.

Baba

The large bungalow Baba had rented for their holiday, in a hilly part of Bihar with big open spaces, had a grass field at the back. At the front a verandah, its roof supported by three columns of pillars, looked out on to a patch of garden. All around the bungalow mango and neem trees cast lovely long shadows that you could skip across with your arms flung out.

No-one was playing in the garden when it happened. They had just finished lunch and Baba had settled down outside to read his newspaper. Ma sat with him enjoying the golden winter sunshine, baby Sheila sleeping peacefully on her lap, Habu, exhausted, resting on a rug on the grass at her side. The sky was a clear, deep blue.

Inside the bungalow, Choto Uncle said, "Let's organize the beds."

The youngest of Baba's many brothers and sisters was not comfortable he said - and he wanted to give each of them a bedroom. Toon was glad, he preferred to be on his own. And his uncle would need his help.

Choto Uncle, nearly as tall as Baba, had to stoop to get through the awkward arched doorways of the bungalow. Being small didn't matter, Toon had enough energy for two and the rope beds were light to carry on their short wooden legs. He grabbed one end.

A sudden, shocking, glorious noise - rushing, roaring. It had to be an aeroplane, and so near! Probably right overhead. Fantastic.

The Tiger Moth danced in his mind, the vibrations started in his head. He dropped his end of the bed and rushed outside as fast as his little legs would carry him, waving his arms wildly, shouting "Aeroplane! *Deko!*"

But there was nothing to see in the clear blue sky. Where was the aeroplane he'd been waiting for? He stopped, puzzled and disappointed.

Choto Uncle was rushing out after him shouting, "*Bhumi compo*. Earthquake!" He felt himself grabbed and held firmly against his uncle's sweating body, with Dada pinned against the other side.

In front of them the earth cracked open and a gaping hole appeared.

CHAPTER 2

It was early in 1934 and seven planets were in the House of Capricorn when the earthquake devastated the state of Bihar - an area the size of England.

The earth roared and heaved for a full three minutes. 25,000 people died, over 3000 square miles were covered with sand, towns and cities were razed and all forms of communication were shattered over 15,000 miles. Many thought the end of the world had come.

Warm subsoil water full of sand forced itself up through blow holes, leaving small volcanic craters and flooding the countryside until it was one vast sea dotted with islands of high ground. Streams of water issued from the wells, choking them with sand. Large fields were thrown into waves with the shock and fissures appeared deep enough to swallow an entire bullock cart and team. Large blocks of land suffered vertical displacement of several inches - or even feet - forcing streams to change their courses. Railway lines were swept away and roads disappeared.

At the time of the earthquake Toon was actually six and a half, not that he knew or cared how old he was. He looked about four, and he wasn't yet at school. His brother had started school at exactly five, but then Dada was quick to learn. When Toon was coming up to five he'd been so small and immature, so mischievous and slow to learn that Ma couldn't imagine any school containing him.

The solution was obvious. She would engage a private teacher and keep him at home until he was seven. Only nobody would know he was seven. He would stand a better chance - at school and probably beyond - if he lost a couple of years. So when it became law to register births, she registered the birth of her second son, Probhat Kumar Ghose ("Prince of the Morning") as 19th August 1929. And nobody was any the wiser, not even Toon himself until half a century later.

His slowness had always worried her. She'd had to wait until he was three and a half to hear him talk.

"There's nothing wrong with Toon," the doctor had said. "He's just happy in a world of his own. He'll talk when he wants to. Leave him alone, he's fine."

The doctor was right.

It was bedtime. Ma and Baba were getting ready for a banquet, Ayah told Toon. She whisked him over to them so that his mother could kiss him goodnight before they went. Ma was wearing a beautiful sari with gold embroidery that he hadn't seen before and when she held out her hands, "Come and give me a cuddle," her gold bangles jingled.

Ma

He wanted to run to her and squeeze her tight but he daren't move.

"Ma, take my pants down, I must go to the toilet."

"Toon! Toon!"

Instead of doing as he asked, she picked him up and started smothering him with kisses. "You can talk, you can talk. A whole sentence."

He felt the new sari soaking against his body but Ma didn't seem to mind. Then Baba rushed in, beaming down at them.

"I told you he's all right. He was desperate so he had to speak."

What was all the fuss about? People were so unpredictable. He went back to his solitary, happy way of doing things, talking in monosyllables, often to himself, and watching.

He watched Baba light his cigarettes and managed to get hold of some matches. The little red toes which had given him his nickname, Toon, wriggled in anticipation. In the warm privacy of the huge four poster bed with the mosquito net pulled up at the top, he experimented. It was fun to see the match lit and even more exciting when it slipped out of his hand on to the sheet. The sheet caught fire. He watched the flame creep along the material, fascinated. He couldn't stop it now.

"*Tumi dushtu chellay*," said Ma wearily. "You naughty boy."

Even the mosquito net was singed.

Ma wanted him to look at those meaningless squiggles again, the Bengali alphabet. She was very patient and he wished he could please her but he wasn't very good at it. He was bored and wanted to play.

The teacher who came to the house was boring too, and more persistent. What was most upsetting about him was the thick lenses in his glasses which hid his eyes.

One hot day he took his glasses off, wiped his face and left the room. What luck. Where to hide them? Quick. Now he would see his teacher's eyes properly, decide whether or not he could be bribed with sweets.

Yes, his eyes were encouraging - perhaps he would like sweets, then they could talk about playing games instead of memorizing stupid Sanskrit grammar.

The teacher was quite a pleasant chap in the end and it was easy to avoid being taught all the time. But Toon was careful not to offend Saraswati, the goddess of learning, as Ma had taught him. If his foot touched one of the books by mistake he would touch the book with his hand and then touch his forehead, as a mark of respect. Hopefully Saraswati wouldn't mind too much that he preferred to play.

Dada was happy to learn - he was doing well at school. He could write things down for their grandfather whose sight was failing. Toon watched his clever brother bend over the page, his tongue poking out of the corner of his mouth in concentration, and for a moment wished he could do the same.

He was as good as anyone at carrying beds though and there wasn't a teacher in sight when the earthquake struck.

"*Bhumi compo.*" Choto Uncle was hurting him, holding him too tightly.

Something terrible, unbelievable was happening. The earth roared and heaved like a furious beast. It had suddenly come alive, huge and threatening and thrilling. The ground where they played simply cracked open. It was breaking up as if some giant hand crumbled it from beneath. He shivered with horror and excitement.

When the noise stopped the silence sounded strange. The sky was still blue and serene. What now? Was the earth-beast going to pounce and swallow them whole? Would nothing be left behind except the sky? He tensed, waiting.

"*Chollo.* Come." Choto Uncle's voice was no more than a squeak.

The three of them ran together, an uncoordinated tangle, he and Dada still clamped under their uncle's arms. They collided with Baba and Ma clutching baby Sheila and Habu as they ran round from the front garden. The bungalow! He gasped. The front half had collapsed like a pack of cards, smashing everything inside to bits - tables, chairs ...

Ma was crying hysterically. They were all safe. Krishna be praised. If they'd been inside it would have been instant death.

Everything had changed. Great splits had appeared in the ground, so deep and dark you could not see to the bottom of them. Perhaps there was no end, perhaps they just went down and down. He could hear the dogs wailing and the people screaming, but Baba wouldn't let them go near the little village that day.

"The earth has opened up."

Herds of cows were running amok, he said, people and animals had been killed, survivors terrified and distraught, buildings destroyed or damaged.

Lying in the tent in the field behind what was left of the bungalow, Toon was too thrilled to sleep much that night. What power there must be to split the ground and tumble houses. Before dawn the earth shook again, but gently this time, and nothing happened.

There was a new world to discover now, of mud bubbles, craters and steam, of roads like dry rivers and new, strange landscapes. It was a big adventure, everyone was too busy to worry about him, and Baba was never there.

Poor Habu was too small to escape so easily. It was a shame he was missing out on all the fun so Toon told him every detail and a few more. "You'll soon be big enough for these things," he said. Habu listened.

One day there was a different sound. Not another earthquake. An aeroplane going over - he was not mistaken this time. The vibration started in his head and his body trembled.

And another one, flying low. Fantastic. Choto Uncle said it was the only way people could see what had happened everywhere - they couldn't travel by land and even if they could it would take too long ... There would be reporters in the aeroplanes, photographers, engineers and officials.

What would the village look like from up in the sky? It was difficult to imagine looking down instead of up. The Tiger Moth and the earthquake - you couldn't think of one without the other, both so powerful. The earthquake was wonderfully fearful and nobody could control it, perhaps not even the gods. And the little aeroplane in the vast sky?

They stayed in the tents for a week. Baba sailed off on his bicycle and disappeared. He had to get back, Ma said. Toon imagined watching him from an aeroplane, a tiny figure pedalling through the steam and sand and water and the gaping holes and collapsing walls. Supposing he was swallowed up? Supposing he never came back?

CHAPTER 3

"*Choop koro*, Toon. Be quiet."

Why didn't anyone want to listen to him? They didn't laugh at him so much these days and they didn't pull him onto their laps so readily either. They laughed at Habu. Habu could do most things now, and he wasn't told to shut up. But you couldn't help loving him. You could rely on his good nature and he was fun to play with. Toon stomped off to find him.

Habu was on the verandah playing with a piece of bamboo. It would be fun to tease him.

Habu turned round, startled, waving his stick. Thump! Toon fell on his face. Large pieces of front teeth shot across the floor. Ma came running. Habu's lip trembled.

"He didn't mean to hit me, Ma. It was an accident."

They weren't just baby teeth on the floor, they were his first grown-up teeth that he'd been so proud of.

"You must take this *vibhuti*, Toon."

The holy powdered ash, given to Ma by a Brahmin priest, was smeared on his forehead. No-one was surprised when his front teeth started to grow again, very strong, for a third time.

They were living in Lucknow and Baba was safe. There had been hundreds of miles of damaged railway track to repair after the earthquake. Baba was such an important man in the Railways.

But look at him now. Who would have believed it? Ma was standing as tall as she could, with a broom clutched in her hand, shrieking up at him.

"Look this is my domain. Yours is outside this house. How dare you speak to me like that?"

Peeping through a slit in the door with Dada and Habu, Toon held his breath.

"If you don't apologize," she said in her shrill voice, "I'll swipe your face with this broomstick and that will sort you out."

Toon shuddered with glee.

Baba looked down with his head bent and his hands together in front of him.

"*Mahp koro*. Forgive," he said to Ma in his big deep voice, and everything was peaceful again.

It was strange. When you saw Ma outside with her sari across her face, meekly walking a few steps behind Baba, you wouldn't know she could shriek.

"Come and get ready, Toon, we're going to have a treat."

A treat! Could it be ...? Was Baba taking them to see another Tiger Moth? A warm feeling began in the pit of his stomach. It was the thing he most wanted to happen.

"We're going to have a picnic in the Banarsi Bagh. Come on. *Tumar kee hoachay*? What's the matter?"

"Nothing, Ma."

At least they were going in the car. There weren't many other cars on the roads and it was fun to weave in and out of the bicycles and the rickshaws and all the animals. He always watched Baba, or whoever was driving, very carefully - he could drive the huge Fiat if only his legs were long enough to reach the pedals. It would be easy.

The road up to the big iron gates where they left the car was lined with stalls selling food. Toon's nose twitched. Corn on the cob was being cooked on a skewer over an open fire and served with salt and pepper and lemon juice. They ate some on their way in, as a starter. No need to buy anything else, Ma had prepared chapattis, and potato, curry and lentil dishes and she had brought lots of salad and fruit - tomatoes, cucumber, little oranges, bananas, his favourite juicy paw paw - and plenty of naan bread.

The animal houses of the zoo were dotted about in the grounds amongst the grass and the trees. He'd seen the animals before. They looked tired and sad, not like the cows and goats and wild boar in the street. They must be bored in such a small space with nothing to do. Habu wanted to climb in with them and had to be dragged away.

A museum stood at the end of the long main drive, with guns outside. Weapons and paintings of people long ago were not at all interesting.

The picnic was good. They found a shady patch on the grass beneath a neem tree and sat cross-legged while Ma, squatting, unpacked the food. Toon ate and ate.

Nobody took much notice of him after that. Dada was reading. Habu had fallen asleep. Toon lay on the grass on his back, warm, half asleep, watching the dark brown kites circling high above him in the blue sky. Perhaps he would be a kite in his next life. A different world up there. He watched the kites dive and soar and stall. The movements seemed kind of familiar. Perhaps he'd already had a life in the air.

The kites were enjoying themselves, not like the animals in the zoo. Imagine flying with them, so peaceful and free.

"*Urbo,*" a voice inside him seemed to say. "Get airborne."

Those kites were clever too. How did they go round and round and up and up without flapping their wings? He watched as they fanned their tails and spread their great wings, fringing them at the edges as if they had little fingers. So many of them gliding together - how did they manage to miss each other?

He could hear a car horn in the distance, like an echo, and bicycle bells and children playing somewhere near on the grass. How hot it was. Still half asleep, but part of him so alert, he fixed on one bird. Chil the kite. He followed it until he felt he was up there with it, one long liquid movement from curved beak to forked tail. He was flying, round and round, higher and higher.

"Time to go home, Toon. Stop dreaming."

As they walked back to the gates with the sun behind them his shadow stretched in front, taller even than Baba. Suddenly he felt so powerful. "Get going." He spread his long, long arms with his fingers fanned, and flapped until he was airborne. Then he fell flat on his face.

Ma was cross. "*Tumar kee hoachay?* What's the matter with you?"

She picked him up and threatened to beat him if he did it again. The shadows in front of them grew longer and longer and the sky was growing a pinkish tinge where it met the mango trees. Why did people have to spoil things? Why couldn't they understand?

Baba tried to teach him to ride a bicycle. Dada and all the cousins had learnt easily but he just couldn't get the hang of it. Baba gave up in the end, said he had no co-ordination or sense of balance.

The days went by. It didn't look as though they were going to see another Tiger Moth. There was no more excitement and now Ma said he would have to go to school soon, after their usual visit to the Calcutta relations. If only something would happen.

But not this, whatever it was. He stared, wide-eyed. Grandmother in Calcutta had thrown herself on the stone floor, wailing hysterically. Ma had disappeared. He smelt fear in the house. It hung in the air.

"Come on, boys," said Dadu grandfather. "We are going to see the Hegenberg Circus."

He and Dada and a cousin went with grandfather. Habu was ill.

Perhaps there was nothing very wrong after all. The tent was enormous, all the seats red velvet. But why did grandfather, so fat and happy, have wet eyes?

There were tigers, elephants, lions.

"Look, there is no cage," said grandfather. "The man in the circus had to vow that if anyone got killed he himself would die."

Toon had never seen such a fantastic looking beast as the lion. And there was nothing to keep it there, no guard. A man in white tights, very fair, stood nearby.

Drums rolled, faster and faster, then the fair man jumped onto the back of the lion from six feet away and the lion roared. The roar went right through him, so magnificent.

It was six o'clock and getting chilly as they left the tent.

It took him a long time to realize what had happened. Ma would not talk. No-one in the family would talk about it.

"*Habu kotai?*" he kept asking. "Where is Habu?"

Was it his fault? He had wanted something to happen.

"God has taken Habu," he was told.

How could God have taken him away when they wanted him so much here? He was sure little Habu would be as lonely as he was. But what could he do?

There was no cure for meningitis.

He would ride that bicycle without Baba. He tried again and again and one day, downhill, he managed to balance on his own. Too good a feeling to stop. He kept going, with the wind rushing against his face. *Urbo*. Get airborne. Keep going, never mind the rose garden at the bottom.

Ma pulled out the thorns and bathed his scratched body.

There were lots of new places to explore when they moved to Allahabad. Number two Railway Bungalow had a long verandah with arches and a lovely garden enclosed by a high wall. The station with its bicycle park was just across the lane and on the roundabout at the top of the road from the station was the huge Catholic church, with the wonderful bells that could be heard from all over.

He had to pass this church as he walked to school every morning. Most of the teachers in the Anglo-Bengali school were Bengali like his family. The head teacher was an old man with a splendid beard, a lovely face and kind eyes. He was a bit bald and tubby but then he was very old, about 55, Ma said.

Most of the year school was from ten to four with lunch provided - raw carrot, seasoned chick peas and fresh ginger - always the same. In the summer months when it became too hot to work after eleven o'clock, school started at six. Even five hours was a long time for him to behave and more often than not he just couldn't manage it. Ma would look worried then.

When Baba was working on the line, Toon slept with Ma in the four-poster bed.

"Ma, wake up."

"Go back to sleep, Toon. It's two in the morning."

"Ma, something's going to happen to the train."

"It's a dream. Go back to sleep."

"But Ma, something will happen."

Why wouldn't she listen? He knew. He knew. Now the sheet underneath him was wet. How had that happened?

Then the foghorn sounded. It went on and on. That meant an accident on the railway. Ma stared at him. They huddled together in front of Krishna in the little glass cabinet, Ma's shrine.

The telephone rang. Baba was safe. Two trains had crashed at Bumrouli station, 16 miles away. Choto Uncle was to drive them to the site of the accident, Baba said.

The trains had collided head on and both reared up like two giant caterpillars. He couldn't get the image out of his mind.

In Allahabad there were no hills. Everyone started from the same point under the big sky, and you couldn't forget your smallness. In Kashmir it was different.

The family spent four months in a tent in Kashmir that year and he discovered hills - climbing up them, jumping off them, reaching for the sky. When he grew up, he promised himself, he was always going to live on hills.

If he stood on top of a hill facing windward with his head slightly forward and his arms outstretched he could pretend to soar. If he leant backwards he would fall down the hill behind - there was no lift.

He had to keep leaning forward, into wind.

It didn't matter here that Dada was so much taller. He didn't even have to climb a tree or sit on a wall to look down on everyone.

And to have to go back to school after such a holiday! Being naughty created a bit of diversion at least. It was so hot. The punkah wallah at the back of the room pulling the strings on the large fan attached to the ceiling was sweating. The punkah wallah was not allowed to talk to them, he was just there. Toon watched him, from his place near the back, fingering the feather in his lap. Should he? Why not?

He poked the feather up the punkah wallah's nose and the poor man sneezed. The fan fell to the side and half of it collapsed on the room. Chaos.

But instead of caning him in private, the teacher put him in a corner and told him to kneel down holding his ears.

The entertainment had been worth a caning, but he couldn't stand this - everyone staring at him in his corner. He suddenly felt so ashamed the tears wouldn't stop spilling out of his eyes. And that made him even more ashamed.

He started behaving better after that. And then he had the dream.

It was such a vivid dream. His class teacher was dead and he was sitting with the other children near the head before the body went on the pyre. A marigold garland had been placed round the neck and the body was dressed in a silk *punjabi*. Such a peaceful face.

Within seven days the teacher really was dead and Toon found himself in the same position by the head as in the dream. It was weird and rather frightening.

Could he be responsible for the things he seemed to know in advance - the accident and the death? Ma said it was all written in the stars. It was destiny. Locked in the almirah were their horoscopes. Everything that would happen to them could be worked out from the stars. There were no secrets. How could that possibly be?

But Habu's had said he would die of a head illness and he had. Dada's said he would be academic and achieve great things. They all knew that was going to happen. He'd overheard Baba and Ma discussing his own horoscope once, in hushed, worried tones. He hadn't understood the words. Why did they never talk to him about it, and what could be in it that was so terrible? Was he going to die too, like Habu and his teacher?

But there was too much happening to think about it for long. Ma's older brother arrived at their door in a tonga.

"Please give me some food."

Toon watched this emaciated uncle with the powerful brown eyes eat everything in sight.

Ma's brother had at last been released from jail.

He'd joined a terrorist group involved in a plot against the corrupt Head of Police. They had no proof against him so they'd planted a revolver on the premises. He'd survived 55 days on a hunger strike to the death with the other political prisoners on the Andaman Islands in the Bay of Bengal. Escape had been impossible through the shark infested-waters surrounding them.

Before that he'd survived needles through his finger nails and other tortures. The brother-in-law, his advocate, forced to witness this and unable to help, died of the horror of it. This uncle must be very strong.

It was awe-inspiring to watch him as he gradually recovered his physical strength. He would sit in the lotus position for over an hour performing a puja. What would it be like to be able to worship like that?

Toon climbed up onto the boundary wall and sat there thinking about it, his legs dangling. He tried to sit still.

Little Sheila was playing down below and hadn't seen him. He smiled to himself as he watched her. She reminded him sometimes of Habu. What could he do to tease her? He wouldn't be able to share her breakfast now Ma had caught him out. That was because Sheila had been so hungry. He used to finish his own breakfast of *muri* and nuts very quickly and go after her.

"I'll pretend to be a monkey on the bed and crouch down with my mouth open. You throw the food in the air and I'll catch."

He would watch her big dark eyes as she threw, laughing. He used to eat a good half of her breakfast.

His heels thumped against the wall.

Soon they would all be moving to a village called Danapur, to another bungalow and another school. Would there be hills? Would they perhaps see an aeroplane?

CHAPTER 4

The large high rooms of the railway bungalow at Danapur were cooled by whirring ceiling fans. The verandah at the back looked out onto a lawn where peacocks strutted. There were several trees, including three or four tall mangoes, and a vegetable patch.

Beyond the garden and the English kitchen in its separate little house and the neat servants' quarters were fields and tennis courts, with a back entrance to the railway station two minutes away. A right turn out of the wooden gates at the front of the bungalow and then right again also led to the station, and the village.

Toon only lasted three days at the first school in Danapur.

The school bully had been tormenting a boy only half his size. The boy was crying. Beside himself with anger, Toon had waded in. "I'll take you on."

The bully had smirked down at him and started pulling his ear. He went berserk. The bully screamed in pain and fear as Toon jumped up and down on his chest. The teachers didn't seem to understand what had happened when they found them like that, but Toon wasn't sorry Baba took him out of the school.

The second school wasn't much better. He would rather have been up a tree or roaming about the fields on his own, perhaps even as far as the paddy fields or the swamps where the mauve water hyacinths grew and the water lilies white as the moon. He dreamed through the lessons or played pranks to relieve the monotony. The other children liked him for that.

Then he saw his chance. A travelling circus had come to the village. Not as grand as the one he'd seen with Dadu grandfather in Calcutta but there were animals and acrobats and all sorts of exciting people. And they would be travelling through India, to places he'd never seen, probably to places with mountains too.

"Will you take me on?"

"Where are you from?" They looked at him suspiciously, even though he'd been wise enough to run away in his oldest clothes.

He gave an uncle's name, one who was very poor. So they agreed to give him a try.

Fetching water from the wells and moving furniture wasn't exactly what he'd imagined work in a circus to be, but it was still exciting to be part of it. He would show them how keen he was. He fetched and carried with as much enthusiasm as he had moved beds for Choto Uncle. So when there was nothing to do they let him in on some of their secrets and taught him balancing tricks.

This was more like it. They said he learnt quickly. It was fantastic. If Dada could see him now!

Only the tigers saddened him. There were three of them in tiny cages, unhealthy-looking, eyes expressionless. He watched them shift miserably from side to side.

They revived an old memory that often popped into his head. It must have happened before he saw the Tiger Moth because he remembered the word "tiger" rolling round in his mouth when Baba told him the name of the aeroplane. The word brought back delicious sensations. "*Bagh*. Tiger."

Whenever he asked about the tiger Ma told him how they were travelling from Asansol to Calcutta through the forests of Durgapur where tigers lived.

He was in the back of the car with Dada and little Habu and Ayah, looking out at the darkness on either side of the narrow asphalt road, half asleep. Ma and Baba were in the front, Baba driving his prized "Rolls" Fiat with its running boards and the huge hunting headlights.

He was jolted awake as the car stopped and Baba got out. There were no servants with them apart from Ayah so Baba had to mend the puncture himself. He squatted by the back wheel.

Excitement surged into Toon's throat, as it always did when something unexpected happened. It was so quiet and dark on the narrow road, miles from anywhere or anybody.

Movement out of the corner of his eye. Suddenly there was this magnificent beast crossing the road, silently, casually, in front of them. He caught his breath.

"*Ogo, bagh esaychay,*" Ma called softly to Baba. "A tiger is coming. Where is your gun? Get back in the car." Her voice was trembling.

The gun was with the luggage in the back where it always was, inaccessible. Toon was glad. He was never ever going to learn to shoot like his father.

"If we leave it alone, it won't do anything," said Baba calmly.

The tiger was staring into the headlights, dazzled. It was so amazing, so thrilling, almost holy, to watch the animal, to admire the enormous stripes, the powerful body and now these eyes that blazed such magnificent indifference. It was the tiger's road and he didn't care about anyone else, or guns, or cars with dazzling lights.

The tiger couldn't have stood for very long but to Toon it was a moment that stretched for ever. Long after the great forest darkness on the other side of the road had reabsorbed the huge form, the eyes blazed on in his mind. "Let nothing get in your way."

These caged circus tigers were different. He must never let himself become like them. "*Urbo,*" the voice inside him said. "Get airborne. Never be caged."

He tried not to think about them as he fetched and carried for the circus performers.

Baba, his eyes dark and angry, found him of course.

"You don't understand anything, Toon. You don't think."

He was dragged home to a distraught Ma.

"How could you, Toon?"

He was puzzled. But the Durgapur tiger's eyes still flashed and the sky beckoned.

There were always trees to climb when school was over. He'd been planning one day to slip away to the outskirts of the village and climb a mango tree that he knew with a sand mound at the bottom of it. He could jump down on to the mound and pretend he was flying.

Then he could wait for the sun to set and the bats to fly over the trees, listen to the sounds of women drawing water from the village well and villagers talking, unseen. Imagination could take you anywhere under a moonlit sky.

"You must finish playing early today," Ma warned.

A private tutor had been engaged to come at seven o'clock to teach him maths because he was so bad at it.

Maths! He wouldn't have time to go to the sand mound now. He would have to make do with one of the mango trees in the garden. The tallest was right by the servants' quarters.

He started to climb, paused when he heard a rustle. It had to be a monkey - nobody could climb higher than he could. He looked up and there, way above him framed against the sky, clutching a thin branch was - surely not - another boy.

Toon stared. The boy seemed intent on climbing recklessly to the top - if he fell or one of the branches broke he would surely be killed. Was he real? How brave he must be.

The boy looked down at him out of a dark round face. He was baring his teeth, fearless, as if to say, "You can never get to the top, ever, like me."

Instantly this boy, Kalu from the servant's quarters, became his hero, his rival and his best friend. As he watched him climb with great confidence right to the top of the sixty-foot tree, a thrilling jealousy crept into his heart.

The top branches swayed from side to side in a gentle breeze and on one of them balanced Kalu, like some hero in a storybook, his wiry body silhouetted against the red sky of a setting sun, arms going up and down and sideways, balancing to prevent a death-fall. Toon held his breath. Even the 45 feet below his own body looked impossibly far.

Kalu beamed down at him, unconcerned.

Suddenly he gave a high-pitched yell, "ooola, ooola, ah - ooh" and began to descend, like a monkey. He drew level with Toon, near enough to make his branch sway. "*Acha hua*?" he said. "How was it?"

Toon didn't know what to reply and Kalu was gone. He slid down from branch to branch. Darkness was falling quickly now the sun had set. He had to climb down fast or he would be late. But Kalu was quicker and had disappeared from sight further down, in the dark.

Would this wonderful boy talk to him again? A servant's child didn't talk to his master's child as Kalu had done up the mango tree, ever.

There was no sign of him at the bottom, the shadows were less defined and a few faint stars were showing. He ran into the house to Ma and saw by the tall rectangular clock that he was on time, just.

Maths! His head was full of Kalu swaying against the sky. There were probably lots of other amazing things he could do. It was a little hurtful that he hadn't waited to talk to him after the climb down, but he had greeted him up the tree. "How was it?" It was fantastic.

There were nine servants, including four trolleymen. The trolleymen were assigned to Baba because he was Transportation Superintendent of the East Indian Railways. His area extended all the way from Jha Jha Railway station to Moghul Sarai Junction near the great holy city of Benares. The trolleymen were picked for their physical strength and balance as they had to lift the trolley onto the rails.

He often watched Baba inspecting the lines. The trolley, weighing a ton or more, was an open carriage of about seven square feet on four iron wheels. Baba would sit on the one chair in the middle of the flat platform, with two men squatting by him. The other two would clutch the grips at the rear of the trolley and push it along, running on the four inch wide rail. If they slipped they would go rolling down the embankment and break their bones. These two would run for a mile, then jump on and the other two would take over. If a train was coming towards them they had to be quick, put the brakes on and lift the trolley off the rails.

The head trolleyman was Kalu's father and his mother worked in the house. They had no other children, which was unusual - most servants had at least three.

Kalu never went to school. Why should he? He was so quick. Quicker even than Toon himself at any athletic feats - running, jumping, picking mangoes from the top branches without falling. The tricks Toon had learnt at the circus? Kalu could perform them already. Kalu could make catapults, he could throw the furthest when they played *dangooli*. He could do anything.

No good telling anyone else how wonderful he was. Ma and Baba didn't approve of the friendship - a servant boy and his master's son! - but if he kept quiet they pretended not to notice. They could see he was happy, whereas at school he couldn't settle at all.

At first he and Kalu seldom talked and when they did, it was mainly about food. He felt content sitting next to Kalu with a bowl of *muri* and peanuts. They were probably about the same age, although Kalu confessed that he didn't know the day or month or even the year he was born either. They could be ten, eleven perhaps. It didn't matter.

They didn't need to mix, they played their own games, they invented new ones. It was fun to have constant competition - Kalu's near-black eyes glowing out of the milky whites, would challenge, excitingly, to run, leap, climb...

When, occasionally, they got together with the village children they were not in competition but team mates, on the same side in *kabaddi*. He felt very proud then. "Tk, tk". Back behind the line in the dust - if you were touched you were dead.

The only good thing about school was being able to read. The stories from the two Hindu epics for example - the Ramayana and the Mahabharata. He and Kalu would discuss all the characters, but their favourite was Hanuman, the monkey god, who could fly through the air.

Hanuman was the son of Vayu, god of the wind. He possessed great powers and he could make himself as small as a speck or blow himself up to be huge, immense, like the biggest cloud in the sky. He went in search of the captured Sita, wife of Prince Rama, leaping over the straits to Lanka to rescue her. How did he fly across the ocean?

He stood on a hill, throwing his whole strength into his foot, then he looked at the sea and directed his mind towards Lanka.

"I shall search and find Sita. I shall fly in the sky and cross the sea."

If only there were hills in Danapur.

"He roared and lashed his tail on the ground, contracted his hind parts, held his breath, pressed down his feet, folded his ears and stiffened his muscles. He rose into the sky with a roar of triumph," Toon read.

Beneath Hanuman his shadow sped across the sea like a huge ship. With his cunning he overcame the obstacles his enemies put in his way, even the she-demon in the sea holding him down by his shadow.

How wonderful to fly like Hanuman. He and Kalu never tired of playing the monkey god. They pressed their feet against the earth, they jumped from the mango tree - not the top - spreading out their arms. And collapsed in a bruised, laughing heap.

Sheila, Choto Uncle, Toon and Dada

CHAPTER 5

The family had been on holiday when he first spotted the baby monkey. It was on its paws on the dusty earth down by the river drinking, unaware of the ripples on the water. The next one was sure to come over its little head. He quickly got hold of it from behind.

The monkey squealed and chattered in alarm, then started gently nibbling his fingers. He was enchanted.

"What have you got now, Toon?" said Ma.

"He's called Manku. Can I have a *colla* for him please?"

Ma gave him one of her finger-size bananas. Manku put it in the little pouch at the side of his throat, to gobble up later when things were less interesting and he had time to eat. Somehow he came back to Danapur with them.

"Oh God, you've got another pet," said Ma.

She must have been remembering the fuss when he'd taken the chipmunk to school, up his jumper.

Manku lived with them for two years and grew from one foot to 18 inches. As soon as he got to know the vast garden he enjoyed complete freedom in it during the day. He had to be restrained at night because of the danger from foxes.

He could walk on his hind legs and hold Toon's hand, his little red face turned up to him, chattering. Toilet training met with no success, but he could be taught almost anything else. He was better at gymnastics than even Kalu, but perhaps his long tail helped. Sitting on Toon's shoulder, he would explore his bulging pouch, gobble up the contents, then have a good scratch. He was someone to talk to when Kalu wasn't there, someone who heard his dreams without making him feel silly.

It was grandfather's fault that Manku had to go.

Baba's father had built a white marble house at Benares, where they often went to stay. Grandfather, Baba told them, had been selected out of 6000 applicants for the accountant's job in the East Indian railways at the beginning of the century. Not originally an accountant, he had studied a famous maths book from the first to last page. He must have been mad.

And grandfather's father, in 1844, had been given the job of surveyor/engineer on the first railway ever in India, from Calcutta to Burdwan. "Where did you learn English?" his interviewers had asked. "Your English is better than ours." He'd read the Oxford Pocket dictionary from front to back and carried 50 exercise books in a canvas bag.

Grandfather

Grandfather the accountant had tracked down a fraud during his time in the railways, at great personal risk, and was highly honoured for his actions. His marble house in Durgakund Road was like a palace, full of mirrors, fine furniture, lavish decorations and a temple - so many things to look at and admire.

But grandfather didn't want the mustard oil Ma rubbed on her children's skin to spoil his marble floor so he built them another house in the grounds.

There was plenty of room for another house in a whole square mile of garden. Toon loved the garden with its 500 lime trees and porcupines and the pathways raised high so that the smooth mangoes and thorny jackfruit could easily be picked. Just to think of the slippery yellow flesh of the jackfruit made his mouth water.

He loved waking up in the early morning to the sounds of crows and foxes and jackals, and best of all the beautiful music wafting across to him in the darkness. Opposite the house they were practising - the tabla player, later to become world famous, the *shanai* (clarinet) player and the *banshi* (flute) player.

Then there was Jethaamoni with his hardware store near the Burning Ghat, where cremations took place by the Ganges. Jethaamoni was an unmarried relative with only his mother and the shop to look after, and time to spare for visiting children. He had plenty of time to read too. He read and read, all the books in the library about foreign countries.

It was as if Jethaamoni had actually tramped the world, not just in spirit, and Toon believed every word of the stories he told on the long morning walks with his dog. In turn he too was transported to all these fabulous places.

"Now off you go on your own."

Jethaamoni had given him and Dada two or three swimming lessons in the Ganges. He wasn't sure he could swim properly yet but he did as he was told and followed Dada out into the river.

His head wouldn't stay up, the water was closing over him, he spluttered and lashed out his arms. Under the water there were strange spirits and demons, like the one that held Hanuman down by his shadow. Where was Hanuman? Help. He was drowning.

He shivered long after Jethaamoni had rescued them and brought them back to the crowded ghat, and Dada looked really scared too. By the Burning Ghat someone held the little tree of lights and blew the conch shell. The powerful note thrilled him. All the evil spirits would be scared away. They might have had to do that for him and Dada.

The ghost stories that Jethaamoni told them at night seemed even more frightening after that. He inched his way closer to Ma as the long shadows cast by the hurricane lamp flickered eerily and Baba played his harmonium, hidden in the semi-darkness.

He thought desperately of Hanuman, his protector, and the story Ma had told him.

A boy, about his age, lived alone with his mother. Dacoits came at the dark of night shouting, "*Arri, arri, arri,*" and attacked the house. They hammered away and pulled down the door. The mother started screaming but the robbers took no notice.

"Ma, don't worry," said the boy. "I'm going to call Hanuman."

Hanuman appeared and just picked up those dacoits and started throwing them away. They were so amazed. They howled. They shouted, "Hanumanji, let us go. Please forgive us."

The mother said she never saw Hanuman but the robbers suddenly left. The boy remembered the incident more or less like a dream.

It was comforting to keep this story at the back of his mind while Jethaamoni talked of ghosts and ghouls in grandfather's big marble house.

For three or four months every year this grandfather stayed with them at Danapur. His room was near the Hindu kitchen - and Manku's favourite tree. Grandfather was not a heavy sleeper. He said he was woken by Manku's "oo, oo, oo," every morning at dawn.

He complained to Ma and Baba about the noise. "If that monkey stays, I go. It should not be kept, it should be allowed to go free."

Let Manku go? How could he bear it?

"Ma, he's the only person I can talk to." Apart from Kalu of course, but it wouldn't be wise to mention that.

Kalu tried to console him. One of the servants knew the habits of monkeys. They would have to prepare Manku so that he could be accepted back in his tribe. Toon knew the tree where he belonged, about 30 miles away, by the river, so that was no problem. But they had to train Manku to respond correctly when he was challenged by the other monkeys, otherwise he would be driven away.

As soon as they saw him the leader and his followers would climb up, silently, and chase him really hard across the trees. When he couldn't stay on a tree and had to drop he would have to fall with a branch in his hand, to mask the smell of humans, otherwise he would be hounded out.

Poor Manku. The monkey obviously couldn't work out what was wrong. Another trick to be learnt?   But why was Toon chasing him so hard?

The sequence was thoroughly rehearsed. With a breaking heart, he took Manku back to the tree where he belonged. He watched the leader chase him, just as the servant had said, and he prayed and prayed. Hanuman must have heard. When Manku fell he had a branch in his hand, so the monkeys walked away. Manku just sat there.

It was agony watching and forcing himself not to run to his pet, until after a while Manku slowly went back to the tree. He couldn't see him after that, and the tears fell.

Did Manku want to be free?   It was just possible he did.

They drove home. On the large covered area outside the front door, facing the drive, Ma had put plants all round the edge. He walked along slowly, making himself count. There were 365.

He must have done something wrong because now they were sending him away from home, but not to freedom. He was to go to a new boarding school in Patna where his cousins lived. Patna was only six miles from Danapur and he'd already attended a day school there, after he'd been thrown out of the second village school for beating up two boys who attacked him.

Dada already went to the Patna seminary because he was so bright. It hadn't been so bad at first as they were taken there past the paddy fields by car.

Driving was easy. He'd been trying it himself for a long time, backing out of the garage, hidden by the side of the house. He was better at backing, though he could move the car forward in first gear pretty well now. If only he dared go faster it would be like being airborne but there wasn't much room in the drive and someone would be bound to catch him.

Later, he and Dada travelled by train to Patna Junction, collected their bikes from the platform and cycled the two miles to the school from there. This all took up so much time that there was less to spend with Kalu. Kalu was to be given a farm job soon. He seemed like a man already.

Kalu's father thought Toon too was "old enough" - 13 perhaps? - and secretly found him a village girl with long dark hair. For a while he was up in the air with the kites, weightless, then Ma's voice, shrill with outrage, pierced his ears and he and the girl were wrenched apart. He found himself chained to the verandah, trembling with shock, until Baba returned. What had he done that was so terrible? Why were they all treating him as though he were some kind of monster? Why was his life so different from Kalu's?

Ma and Baba weren't any more pleased with his progress at the Patna school than at the local ones and so now they were sending him away. Why did he need to go to school anyway? Kalu had never had any lessons and look at what he could do.

Ma had once told him that Tagore, the great Bengali poet, hadn't liked school either. When he was young he soaked his feet in the garden pond day after day to make himself ill to avoid going to school. He'd heard his mother saying, "Don't get your feet cold and wet or you will be ill." It hadn't worked at first but eventually he succeeded.

Perhaps his mother knew that he would be a great man anyway - it was probably in his horoscope. Whereas Ma - well whatever she knew she wouldn't say and it didn't look as though there was anything he could do to change things. Manku was back in the wild for ever and he and Kalu were being parted. And now he was to go to yet another stupid school and he'd have to sleep there as well, sleep without hearing Ma blow on the conch shell every night to keep the evil spirits away.

CHAPTER 6

A black kite circled peacefully above St Xavier's School in Patna and the sky to the west was tinged pink. Under the spreading neem tree in the middle of the grass courtyard Sumantro played his flute, his friends listening at his feet.

Now the old familiar Bengali Khawro Vayu, now Swanee River, and now a haunting folk tune again. The music lingered in the warm air.

It wasn't a bad place. His room looked down on the courtyard with its splendid neem tree and the bench seat all round it. Behind it he could see the banyan tree with a hint of red in its foliage. The school was Catholic, run by American Fathers.

"Probhat? Is that the correct pronunciation?" asked the Principal, Father Moran, at his interview.

He wore a long white robe, his eyes were deep blue and his lips so deeply red he could have been wearing lipstick.

"Is the whole length of the Ganges holy, or just a part of it, such as Benares?"

"The entire length, Father," he'd replied - and was promptly admitted.

When Sumantro had gone missing from school, they were told he had smallpox and when he returned all he could do was croak. The flute became his voice.

What would it be like never to speak properly again? Suppose that had happened to him? He had been very ill himself not so long ago. It had started when the brakes failed on his bicycle, not long after his humiliation on the verandah.

He was riding from the bungalow, not right towards the village but left towards the cantonment. The ground sloped steeply down to paddy fields on either side. There was no one about. He pedalled faster and faster. "*Urbo*," said the voice. "Get airborne."

He was taking off, soaring into the sky ... He crashed into the tree before he'd actually seen it.

A vein was severed in his head and he coughed blood. He became ill with double pneumonia, and that's when the asthma started.

Gradually school stopped feeling like a punishment. It wasn't so bad. The work still seemed rather pointless but he knew how to liven it up. The other boys had come to realize there wasn't a dare he wouldn't carry out, and he couldn't let them down, could he? Then Father Wroblewskye, the class teacher, seemed to value his talents for sport. Father encouraged him and that made him try even harder, especially at baseball. Also there were outings when Father took some of them on the Ganges. Only he and Gautam Bir were strong enough swimmers to be allowed to swim from the boat. That felt good too.

If life got too boring or he needed to be on his own, it was easy to slip away, not out of the front of the school to the road and the large grass Maidan, but out of the back. The Ganges was not far away, or he could climb up the strange beehive-shaped building, the old Victorian grain store. The steps spiralled round the outside of it and from the little platform at the top he could see the school behind him and the wide, wide river in front. He could look down on the rickshaw wallahs pedalling their vehicles along the road and the saris laid out on the grass to dry and the people going about their business unaware that he was watching them.

But he was stuck in one place. What would it be like to look down on all of India like this, to fly over all of the world?

He descended the spiral staircase as slowly as an old lady, then wandered about in a dream, the big round sweet he'd brought with him still in his hand.

No warning. The kite swooped down from nowhere, shocking, huge. Everything scattered, the *jilebi* dropped from his hand and broke. No time to recover. Another swoop and the kite snatched up the scattered pieces of sweet. Frightening, fantastic.

The summer holidays of 1942. He thought he was thirteen. His exploits with Kalu seemed like memories from another life, a childhood that he was being forced to leave behind. But he knew as he sat alone in the mango tree that he would never forget his amazing friend as long as he lived.

"*Tik koray poshak poro,*" said Ma. "Dress up properly."

A sort of tense suppressed excitement hung in the air at the bungalow. He looked at Ma and then changed his clothes without a word. Dada and Sheila were doing the same. Their appearance seemed to satisfy Ma. She was preparing sherbet. Somebody important must be visiting, but who? And why had they not been told?

Baba and the Divisional Superintendent came first. More cars were drawing up outside.

A small frail man in a dhoti alighted from one of these cars. Toon gasped.

The dhoti was neatly tucked above his knees and he wore a thin chaddar round his body. A pocket watch dangled from his waist and the familiar lathi was in his hand. The bald head, the wheat complexioned face with the toothy smile and the round glasses over the beautiful, powerful eyes.

It was unbelievable. Mahatma Gandhi, the great man whose eyes looked lovingly at him from the front page of nearly every newspaper, as if he knew him personally - this great man was actually entering their drawing room.

Then Ma was calmly serving cool sherbet and sweets to Mahatma and all the Congress dignitaries who accompanied him and Baba was introducing Dada and him and Sheila.

After Dada, he bent and touched Gandhi's feet, wiping dust from his toes, and then touching his own head. Never had this custom meant so much.

He couldn't turn away from those powerful eyes for a second. He could feel the goodness, the loving, as if it were something to be clutched out of the air.

Gandhi chatted with Ma and then he was asking them where they were studying, what class they were in - and school didn't seem so pointless after all.

Suddenly it was over. They left by the back verandah, through the garden and out of the bungalow's back wicket-gate to the goods gate of the railway station. Gandhi walked with the family, one hand on Ma's shoulder and his long lathi in the other. At the station they touched his feet again and he put his hand on each of their heads and blessed them.

"Concentrate on your studies," he said.

The train was already at the platform, lined up so that the rear third-class compartment meant for Mahatma was near the goods gate. He and his entourage always travelled third class.

He blessed them all once again by raising his hand and then they seated him away from the window. He couldn't be seen. Somehow people on the platform realized he was there and ran to his compartment shouting. *"Jai Mahatma. Jai Mahatma."* But the train was already moving.

Gandhi had come to address a meeting on the Maidan in Patna, opposite St Xavier's. Disturbed by the increasing unrest and terrorist activity against the British, he wanted to reiterate his strong belief in non-violence.

The crowds waiting for him even on Patna railway station had been so overwhelming that Baba, the other railway officials and police had found it very difficult to extricate the frail Gandhi and in the jostle that followed he became ill.

To avoid the same thing happening when the meeting was over, the top ministers of the Bihar Government secretly agreed with railway officials that Gandhi should join the train at Danapur instead of Patna. Baba took a leading role in making these arrangements, and the bungalow was ideally placed.

Toon dreamt that night of eyes, deep-set white-fringed yellow tiger eyes with blue-green pupils, flashing, challenging; Baba's dark, angry eyes as he dragged him back from the circus; Gandhi's knowing, loving eyes. Now he couldn't see them any more because the water was closing over him and his eyes wouldn't open under the water for fear of the demons and spirits there. He struggled to the surface. He wanted to see the sky.

Another year.

"Concentrate on your studies," Gandhi had told them.

He did try, but it was difficult. Dada didn't find it difficult, he was doing so well at his college, just as his horoscope predicted. Sheila wasn't creating any problems - his little sister was growing up and getting more beautiful all the time. She would be like Ma one day.

Then Baba was awarded the title of Rai Bahadur like grandfather before him, not for uncovering frauds but for restoring railway communications in the Bihar region in the quickest possible time.

It wasn't an earthquake that had hit the state of Bihar this time but the escalating unrest and violent disturbances which so worried Gandhi. With the roads and railway line blocked, Bihar was cut off from the rest of the country for more than three weeks.

It struck Toon suddenly one evening as he watched his father fingering his glass - Ma said he drank too much - how drawn his face had become. He wasn't supposed to look so vulnerable. Where was the old god-like Baba? But of course he was just as proud of him as the others were.

Everyone else in the family was doing well. It was hardly surprising they took no notice of him.

But there was one thing he was good at, and he wasn't in the right place when it mattered. Neither he nor Gautam Bir were on the boat when Ahmed fell into the Ganges on one of Father Wroblewskye's trips. Ahmed was in the water for six minutes and now he was dead. It was impossible not to keep looking at his empty chair. Was it in his horoscope that he should drown, that Toon should not be there to save him? It seemed so unfair.

The English Cemetery in Patna was so peaceful, another world. He first discovered it when he'd been to see his cousins in the holidays. Their house backed onto the cemetery and when he stayed with them he used to slip out at dusk or at dawn and creep among the graves, frightening himself with memories of Jethaamoni's ghost stories. How long could he last before he ran back, stupid with terror?

Now he just went there for peace. He didn't know much about the Christian gods. His own Hindu gods were alive and real. They sat there, colourful and re-assuring, in Ma's shrines and in his mind. The pale, delicate-featured Krishna, dressed in scarlet and gold, played his pipe in Ma's little glass cabinet and

looked down on the conch shell and the portraits hung with
bright red *jaba* flowers on the table below him.

Then there were the many images of Shiva in the temple.
These gods had their problems and their longings too. He
knew that from the stories about them. He was beginning to
appreciate them more, not just Hanuman but Shiva's son
Ganesh with the elephant head, Visnu who rode Garuda king
of the birds, Durga the ten-armed goddess riding a tiger, Kali
with her red tongue and necklace of skulls and especially Shiva
himself. Perhaps Shiva with his trident and his third eye would
understand him like no-one else could.

They were soon to move to Calcutta, not to the house where
Ma had been born and where she had returned to give birth to
each of her children, but to another house, 85B Lansdowne
Road. He would have to leave the fields of Danapur and St
Xavier's with all his friends and start again in huge, over-crowded
Calcutta. Now it was time to leave he realized what he was
losing.

He would be attending another St Xavier's there, St Xavier's
College in Park Street, but he would live at home. At least the
same vast sky would be above them and the same dream in his
head.

He couldn't imagine how, but one day he'd fly.

CHAPTER 7

St Xavier's College, Calcutta, was built round a square field. The classrooms overlooking it held little interest for Toon. It was on the field that he enjoyed himself and on the field that he excelled.

"*Ghora da*. Big brother horse," they shouted. "*Chollo*. Come on."

He earnt his nickname as a back in football, charging all over the place. He had so much strength and energy for all sports, in spite of his asthma.

At the weekend he was free of college. He could fly his kites, kites made of paper on a single string, but a string as long as possible so that the kite could fly as high as a bird, up, up, up into the sky. As he paid out the tugging length, his eyes following every movement, it was easy to imagine that it was himself up there.

This kite was a fighting kite. He'd mixed glue with finely ground glass and laboriously coated the whole length of string, wearing his special gloves. It was sharp as a knife. He played with the others at trying to cut his opponents' kites free and save his own.

Somebody managed to slice through his. He watched it float along, free, and fall onto the roof of a house. He ran to the house and the family invited him in, a large extended family with four boys older than himself.

"Where do you come from?" they asked.

"I'm a Bengali."

"Yes, we can tell you're Bengali but you have a different accent. You must come from Bihar or the Provinces."

Yes, he was brought up in the country where there was space and freedom. And he didn't want to discuss accents, he only wanted his kite. But he had to be polite and drink their tea. Besides, they had a much bigger, higher roof than his.

"Come any time you like," they said. "Come and fly kites from here."

They became firm friends and he grew better and better at flying his kite, so sensitive to its movement that it became like an extension of his own body. But he was always careful to keep his feet on the roof. So many boys in Calcutta had got carried away and toppled over the edge, sometimes killing themselves.

"If you're keen on sports," said Baba when Toon kept disappearing, "we'll have a badminton court on the lawn and set up table-tennis on the verandah."

Toon had been sleeping in the same room as Dada since they'd moved to Calcutta but they'd kept mostly to themselves. Sport was an interest they had in common and now they could both play together with their friends. Toon did whatever Dada told him to do. That was proper for a younger brother and Dada always seemed to get things right anyway.

Baba seemed pleased that his sons were getting on so well. But he still looked tired and drawn. The strain of the last few months was telling. When he was struck down it was a terrible shock, but in a strange way it was a relief too.

A brain haemorrhage, the doctor said. The left side of his body was weak and he didn't seem to know what was going on - Baba, who always had everything under control.

Ma decided they would travel by train with an uncle and Toon and Sheila back to their relatives in Patna. From there they would hire a car to go to the hot springs at Rajgir. They would stay in Rajgir and Baba could take baths in the holy water and be cured.

A Model "T" Ford with its long nose and smart canvas roof was hired at Patna, but a driver? No-one could be found. Ma was desperate.

He felt strange, warm sensations swelling his body. "Don't worry, Ma," he whispered. "I can drive."

"You? You can't drive."

They wouldn't punish him now for "borrowing" Baba's car and practising in and out of the garage at Danapur.

Here was his chance to drive on a proper road and be really useful too. The roads to Rajgir were very narrow, but there were hardly any cars, only bicycles and carts and animals. It felt good behind the wheel, with Ma and Baba and Sheila in his care. Growing up wouldn't be all bad.

They stayed near the pink temple and the hot springs for ten days. Baba didn't know where he was when he went for his first dip, Toon supporting him on one side and Ma on the other. They led him gently down the steps into one of the pink stone tanks, until they were all nearly submerged in the hot, holy water. It felt good, peaceful.

Only half an hour afterwards, Baba started looking round. It was amazing. The gods were so powerful.

They took Baba to the hot springs every morning and afternoon. He gradually recovered until after seven days he was able to walk up the steps with them above the springs, to where the air was cooler.

Toon often came up here alone when Ma didn't need him. He climbed as nimbly as a goat and at the top he could look down on the pink temple and the springs and the trees and the tiny people below, across at the mountain on the other side of them and green fields stretching way into the distance until they met the sky. And the sky! Big fluffy white cumulus clouds against the clearest of blue.

To see Baba walking up here was like a miracle.

Toon loved wandering off on his own in this lovely place, climbing up, running down, but he never got lost and frightened himself, as he had done so often as a child. If only they could live here instead of Calcutta.

Baba made a full recovery. They went to the Brahmin priest at the Kali temple with offerings of sweetmeats and marigolds, listened to him read the holy words from the Mahabarata. Offerings were made again to Kali and Shiva back in Calcutta - bright red *jaba* flowers, rice, papaya and bananas - and life went on as usual.

Although the war was too far off to affect them very much directly, it was exciting to hear about it. The American troops had their barracks near the house, but most thrilling of all was what was happening on the Maidan, the huge grass park with the Victoria Memorial at one end and the Ochterlony monument, the infamous Black Hole, at the other.

The wide, straight Red Road which cut through the middle of the Maidan was closed to traffic and was being used as a runway.

It was like a dream come true. Three Hurricanes could take off together on this asphalt road. The area was really out of bounds but that didn't matter. He managed to sneak in and watch the Hurricanes and a few Spitfires take off and rise to 15,000 or 20,000 feet for dog-fight practice. If only he was old enough he would have been a fighter pilot. He would have really gone for it.

Then the Japanese bombed the industrial estate of Calcutta and a black-out was imposed at night. Sometimes during the day the fighters would fly over, glinting in the sun. Toon did not want to stay in an air-raid shelter - he wanted to go outside and have a look, but he was not allowed.

St Xavier's College was less exciting. He had to resit exams several times, although if he made up his mind to pass like he had done in geography, he could. His great friend Kutu Das tried to keep him on the straight and narrow, but studying didn't seem very relevant somehow. What was he going to do until he could achieve his dream? And how was he going to achieve it?

There were peaceful places to think, even in Calcutta. The cemetery, deserted and overgrown like a jungle, or Lake Rabindra, not too far from the house, where white egrets walked on lily leaves as if they were walking on water. To break away from the family was utter disobedience and he didn't have the guts to do it yet. One day he would be free.

"Join me in a puja," Ma said, and with Sheila and Dada he would receive the red spot on his forehead, powder mixed with sandalwood paste, to be blessed. They would give offerings to Krishna in the glass cabinet and Ma would chant a mantra in Sanskrit.

More often he would sit by the shrine in Ma's little prayer room, alone and quiet, and read from one of the great holy epics, not always about his favourite Hanuman. Peace would calm him.

But the turbulence was only pushed beneath the surface. It manifested itself in illness, especially his asthma.

And now he couldn't ignore the disturbing things that were happening in the whole of India. India was to be free too, but there was tension in the air, not freedom. His nights were plagued with bad dreams.

One dream was especially vivid. Six Muslim dhobi wallahs and tailors who lived among the Hindus in their own community of shacks, all lay dying on the dust outside and a boy was kicking one of them in the head until the blood spurted in all directions, covering the others. Toon went for this boy. He wanted to knock the boy senseless. He would have been killed himself if he hadn't been a Hindu.

Krishna and the conch shell

Gandhi was almost a lone voice against partition. Nehru had been invited to form an interim government and, although he'd included two Muslims, Jinnah was convinced that the Hindus couldn't be trusted. He called for "direct action" to achieve Pakistan. It was then, in August 1946, that the dream became horrifying reality. Thousands of people were killed in Calcutta. Muslims set about slaughtering Hindus and Hindus retaliated.

Attlee announced early in 1947 that the British would leave no later than the following June. Mountbatten, realizing partition was the only way to avoid a massive civil war and afraid that delay would only cause more violence, advanced the date for the British withdrawal to August 1947. Baba read the newspapers every day from cover to cover but he never discussed the news with his younger son, just as he never discussed the contents of his horoscope, firmly locked in the almirah.

What would independence mean for India? The Act had been rushed through the British Parliament and now millions were making for the frontier. The greatest exodus on earth was taking place. Hindus from East Bengal tried to reach Calcutta, Muslims from West Bengal fled in the opposite direction to what was to be East Pakistan. These uncontrolled streams of refugees resulted in near-hysterical mob violence, unthinkable atrocities. Baba's friend was stabbed buying a book in a Muslim area.

Would all this result in a better world? Or would there be war against the British, or civil war - Indian against Indian? Thoughts of Gandhi returned again and again, Gandhi on hunger strike here in Calcutta to try to bring everyone to their senses. His body was so frail to start with, and his beautiful eyes would be so sad. For the freedom he'd worked so hard to achieve to result in the violence he'd always abhorred must be breaking his heart.

Would personal freedom be so costly to achieve? Were dreams always doomed to disappoint? My own turmoil, so insignificant, reflected the greater turmoil of India - agitation, sadness, conflict, fleeting hope. It took an enormous toll on body and soul. Inside my head was the thumping of tired feet, my weight plummeted to seven stone and the asthma worsened. I was suffocating from lack of air, lack of freedom, tortured by the all-too-real suffering I witnessed and the unreal, uncertain future. I was growing up.

By the end of 1947 the violence had died down. Independence Day was celebrated on 26th January, 1948, with brilliant fireworks at midnight, parties and rejoicing. Four days later Gandhi was assassinated by a Hindu fanatic.

CHAPTER 8

I pedalled faster and more furiously. Why had they spoilt the dream that was so much a part of me? It had been locked inside, deliciously secret, for so long and now as soon as it was out in the open, "I'd like to learn to fly," they'd said, "No."

"No?"

"Concentrate on your studies. You've already written off two cars."

There had to be more to it than that. Baba and Ma exchanged fearful looks and their faces became set. It was almost as if they'd been expecting the request.

"Flying? Never."

That was the end of it as far as Baba was concerned. It was an effort to quell the anger bubbling up inside me. In a Hindu household a father's word was law even when his children were grown and married. To disobey should be unthinkable.

Impossible to keep pedalling at such a rate. I had to slow down, puffing and panting, to recover. What was I doing? How could I be so utterly disobedient? There was a tightening in my chest. Why was Baba so adamant that I should never fly? My thoughts veered, as they often did, to the mysterious horoscope locked in the almirah. If it was something to do with that, why not tell me? Why treat me like a child? I was almost twenty after all, wasn't I?

The breathing was easier now. Time to speed up. However scared I was, I couldn't wait to get to the cantonment and the airport. The need to be near an aeroplane at last, perhaps even to touch one, was overpowering. And this was only to be an inquiry - there wasn't any question of actually doing anything, so what was the harm? The 16 miles on my bicycle was like a long dream, speeding, slowing down, excitement, fear.

Squadron Leader Bose of Barrackpur Flying Club was well known, and he flew aeroplanes. But he was a kind, quite ordinary man, not the god-like creature I'd been expecting.

"How much does a lesson cost, please?" My own voice echoed round my head, unreal.

"Ten rupees an hour, in a Tiger Moth."

"Oh, a Tiger Moth?"

The vibration began somewhere deep inside. Wasn't this a sign - the same aeroplane that had started it all? I fought to steady my voice.

"Where do you keep your aeroplanes?"

"In that hangar. It's an ex-Royal Indian Airforce hangar."

"Can I go and have a look?"

"Of course you can." He led the way.

"Kumar here is learning to fly. He'll take you round."

"What do they call you, then?" said Kumar. "What's your name?"

"Probhat Ghose." It was more of a whisper.

"Right Probhat. So you're going to fly."

The trembling again. "I don't know yet. It's only an inquiry. I've got no money with me."

We walked to the side door of the hangar. Two beautiful Tiger Moths. My God, it was like bumping into old friends you haven't seen for years, so personal. I was gripped by an overpowering desire to touch one of them, the tip of the wing, the propeller.

Kumar took the leather cover off the nearest open cockpit and pointed out the instruments.

"Where do you sit?" I asked. How could this conversation sound so ordinary?

"I sit behind and the instructor sits in front. You go solo like that."

Kumar had gone solo after five hours.

"That's amazing, isn't it?"

"I've been a bit lucky and Mr Bose is a very good instructor."

"Do you mind if I sit in the cockpit?"

Foot on the black part of the lower wing, stand on the seat and then slide down. So easy.

"But how can you see if the instructor is in front of you?"

"You can see all right. You'll be taught."

But I was already flying, with Kumar forgotten - until I noticed the strange looks he was giving me. Embarrassed, I climbed out quickly, but not before I'd reverently touched the wing above me.

"Can I touch the propeller?"

"If you want to." A strange look again, but who cared?

Two smooth brown arms ready to whirl, with a metal cone in the middle. Two smooth brown arms shouting to be touched.

"Thank you."

"We'll see you again then?"

How could I come and how could I not come?

War waged inside me on the long ride back, but the outcome was already determined.

Ma was walking into the kitchen when I came up behind her. I gave her a big hug and my hand slid to the end of her sari, gently untwisted it and stole ten rupees from her little cache.

The bicycle ride seemed even longer than the last time, speeding, slowing. Somehow, though, here I was in a leather helmet, sat in the cockpit behind Mr Bose, examining the gosport tube through which we would communicate.

In an aeroplane at last. Actually sitting in an aeroplane.

The engine noise surprised me. It wasn't the droning familiar from the ground, but an exciting, urgent kind of noise. A breeze cooled my sweating face. Mr Bose was feeling all the controls, muttering something about full, free movement. His head blocked my view. My hands clenched tighter and my heart pounded as Baba's furious eyes seemed to hover in the air before me. What on earth was I doing here?

The engine noise increased, a rush of wind hit my face and we were airborne.

An overpowering sense of belonging mixed with the fear and exhilaration.

We climbed higher and higher, the trees and houses shrank. The noise of the engine and the propeller and the slipstream and the wind blowing past drove everything else from my head.

"We have level flight now. Can you see ahead of you? Look to the side - the wings are level. Look at the airspeed - 80 miles per hour. We level at 2000 feet, rpm 1900."

"Yes."

Outside the sky was blue, blue, blue. It was about one o'clock and very clear. Mr Bose followed a route along the Ganges where tiny boats floated. Millions of people would be going about their business down there, intent on praying, fighting, loving, cooking curry. But I couldn't see them. They did not exist for me.

Yet I could see from above the pattern of everything down there, how it all joined up, as if I were god, or perhaps Chil the kite.

"Put the stick forward and the nose goes down, speed increases and we're losing height. Like a bicycle going down hill. Did you see that?"

"Yes."

"Put your hand on the stick and feel what is happening."

Mr Bose moved the stick back and the nose came up, he moved the stick from left to right and the wings tipped. He moved the rudder with his feet. It was difficult to concentrate with such a fairyland outside.

What right had we to be up here, held in the sky as if by magic?

We gently turned over the water back towards the airfield, like a sequence in a dream.

"Now we're going to descend. Have your hand on the controls."

A beautiful, smooth landing. I would never ever be able to fly like that. Squadron Leader Bose might look ordinary, but he was indeed a god.

He was also a member of the Rotary Club of which Baba was Chairman that year. They met in the Grand Hotel, Calcutta.

"I'm glad your son Probhat is so keen to learn."

"But you are a flying instructor."

The fury in Baba's voice when he returned home was unmistakable.

"*Aydikay esho.* Come here."

His angry eyes bore down on me.

I stood in front of him, hands folded, looking at the ground.

"How dare you disobey me? You'll never fly an aeroplane again."

That was all. Baba walked away. The darkness closed in.

CHAPTER 9

My ambition was thrust down into the darkness again. I watched the birds, how they soared, how they dived, how they landed and how they turned, especially the kites.

My gaze always strayed upwards and every little change recorded itself in my mind - the colours and shades, the shapes of the clouds, their constant dissolving and re-creation, their progress across the sky. It became second nature to forecast the weather.

Banned from the sky I read and dreamt about it, took imaginary lessons in imaginary aeroplanes, spread my bird wings. It was so frustrating, impossible to convey my longing to Baba or even Ma.

The frustration made me ill again. Sometimes it was a real struggle to breathe for two hours at a time. Ma would treat me with steam and rub mustard oil on my back. Ayurvedic medicine for asthma simply knocked me out, I had grown so thin and weak. I felt wretched. Lord Shiva must be punishing me for some terrible deed in a former life.

Religion was becoming more and more of a comfort, but all the offerings and pujas made no difference. What sacrifices did Kali demand then? God was not helping me.

"I'm taking you to see Mr Bannerjee," said Baba.

Mr Bannerjee, a yogi, operated in the Health Centre near Rabindra Lake. I undressed as I'd been told and sat next to a beggar boy who was even thinner than I, with all his ribs showing. The yogi looked at us both and smiled. His eyes were part of the smile, penetrating, inspiring, kind.

He dealt with the beggar boy first, leaving me to wait for half an hour. I watched all the athletic people passing by and envied them their beautiful bodies.

The yogi seemed to read my thoughts. "Listen to me carefully. You will get back to normal health if you carry out what I tell you to do. First, throw away all the medicines you've got. Who does the cooking?"

"Cook and my mother."

"Tell them you must eat your last meal before sunset and have nothing before sunrise. Cut out any form of sweet, meat, fish, eggs, nuts and milk products."

There were about 25 people in the group I was to join. They met every morning, seven days a week. First they would fill up their stomachs with lukewarm water and put two fingers down their throats to make themselves gag so that the water spilled out. Then they performed yogic exercises. They were taught *neti*, the art of inhaling lukewarm salt water up one nostril and letting it flow out of the other.

The transformation began in me within a week.

This regime continued every morning for six months and at the end of it I was a very fit man. Although I still relied heavily on religion, talking with the yogi had made me realize that I had to help myself. God couldn't do it all.

There was so much energy inside me now and it couldn't be directed, yet, to achieving my aim. I'd always been good at sports, but lack of stamina in running when my asthma worsened had let me down. So concentrating on table-tennis seemed the obvious course. I decided to go all out for it and so did my neighbour, Saroj. We made an unlikely pair - me thin and wiry and Saroj short and stocky with tremendous strength.

We went every night to practise upstairs at the YMCA in the Chowringhee. We bribed the porter with sweets, samosas, anything we could salvage to let us in a couple of hours before opening time. Sometimes we were free to play during the day as well and then we would stay there for up to ten hours.

The stars would practise on the next table. We were too much in awe of them to dare speak. But they began to notice we were always there and started to talk to us, said we could help them by giving them matches. Saroj played a defensive game, I attacked.

I slashed away at my frustration with the bat.

Baba found me a job - apprenticeship training for ground engineering in Dum Dum Airport, Number Nine Hangar, at 60 rupees a month. Did he think working with aeroplanes would cure me of my urge to fly, or what? It was an extraordinary move, fuelling my frustration, putting temptation in my way.

I tried, but after the first month I lost all interest in the job. Ground engineers did not normally go up, as Baba knew, but scrounging a flight as a passenger in the twin-engined Dakota was not too difficult. Then there were three or four test flights as a C class mechanic, sitting behind the cockpit when engines had been changed overnight.

"How is my son getting on?" Baba asked the Chief Engineer.

"Not very well. His mind wanders. But he likes flying so much that we make sure he gets some trips, on test flights."

"What did you say?"

Dark angry eyes turned on me again.

Baba stopped the flights. The course held no further interest. His almost hysterical opposition to any idea of my flying was still puzzling. It was not like Baba to be so cruel without a reason. Somehow I would have to get away, away from the sphere of his influence.

Meanwhile long train journeys fuelled my desire for travel - by 1952 Saroj and I were both state table-tennis players, although not partners, playing exhibition matches all over India. There were the World Championships in Bombay and then the Doubles Championships at home in Calcutta.

We didn't beat our opponents in Calcutta, but we extended them to a five-set match and it was the best game I ever played. It hurt that Baba wasn't there. He didn't come once to watch me play.

There was no earning capacity with table-tennis, except in professional coaching. But it was obvious that my heart was not in engineering and frustration was building up. So I'd been allowed to quietly leave Dum Dum.

Baba's thoughts were elsewhere. His father, my grandfather of the marble house in Benares, had died early one winter morning while he was staying with us. It was so unsettling to see Baba howl, but somehow reassuring too.

From our house it was about one and a half miles to the Burning Ghat where the dead were cremated. I'd been there a dozen times before. My worst memory was of following the body of a three-year-old in the warm darkness of four in the morning, my little friend who'd died, like Habu, of meningitis.

With grandfather I had a definite function to perform. The Brahmin priest had come by eleven. The body, in a silk loincloth and decked with sweet-smelling marigold flowers, was ready on the stretcher. Four of us, one at each corner, lifted the stretcher onto our shoulders and the slow walk to the Ganges began. The chanting started then, *"Hari Krishna, Hari Rama"* and coins were thrown for all the beggars.

At the Burning Ghat a site had been prepared - a rectangular trough in the earth about six feet by three, and two feet deep. This was filled with sandalwood, piled up to two feet above the ground. Grandfather's body was taken off the stretcher, laid on this funeral pyre and tied down to prevent the body contracting when the fire roared. Baba, the eldest son, lit a stick of sandalwood to start the fire and placed it in grandfather's mouth - sacred flames to take the pain away. Such a peaceful face now. The Brahmin priest chanted the mantra in Sanskrit *"Om Shanti, Om Shanti"*

It was our duty, the four young bearers, to stand one in each corner with sticks in our hands as the fire took hold, in case anything happened.

Flames leapt and, oh God, Grandfather sat up.

The body, not tied properly, had contracted with the heat. Quickly we beat it down with the sticks. Baba did not see - he was looking the other way, howling.

That was it. Grandfather had escaped. Now we had to help release his soul. No shaving, no paring of nails, no wearing of leather for twelve days.

On the thirteenth day the ash would be put in an urn, the beautiful mantra chanted again and the urn carried away on the Ganges. *"Om shanti, shanti, shanti. Om shanti."* Then the shaving of heads and the feast.

But for those twelve days, barefoot, we talked often of grandfather and what he had achieved. There was talk too of his father, Nandan, the one who'd read the Oxford Pocket Dictionary from front to back and got himself an engineer's job on the first railway in India.

His grandfather had been Nandan too, eldest son of Rajah Ghose of Bali on the Ganges. I loved this story as a child. Rajah Ghose had palaces and elephants and horses and nine pots of gold *mohar*. Money-hungry relatives plotted to dispose of the whole family. But faithful servant Hari overheard the plot, stole enough money to give nine-year-old Nandan a good education and escaped with him across the three-quarter-mile wide Ganges.

The rest of the family were all wiped out by poison but the line was saved. Nandan went on to build another empire, all by himself.

How could I live up to these adventurous ancestors? I hadn't made a very auspicious start. Already in my twenties, my life was drifting away, not amounting to anything. Baba was right. Was it that I hadn't been given the chance or that I didn't make enough effort to let it happen?

Nandan's story talked to me in a different way now. Nandan had made a new start. No family to tell him what to do. Sooner or later I would have to follow his example.

It was 1953 and Baba was consulting the stars. He had quite a reputation as an amateur astrologer. People even brought their children to him for advice about arranging marriages.

Dada was safe - his horoscope predicted that he would never marry, so Ma and Baba would leave him alone. My own horoscope was never discussed - they had better not arrange anything for me.

But this consultation of the stars had nothing to do with marriages. It concerned a family outing.

"Nothing can go wrong," I heard Baba say to Ma. "Even with Toon. Not on this date."

We were going to visit the holy place of Bhubaneswar in Orissa. It would have taken twelve hours by train. It was going to take us only one hour - we were actually flying!

The aeroplane was a Dakota DC3. This Dakota had been world famous for carrying cargo and troops but had been converted for passenger flights after the war and now seated about 50 people.

Even the sight of it made my heart beat faster. And the noise of the engines! Had Baba imagined that my desire to fly was just a passing fancy? Had he no idea how I would feel? Of course he didn't know the books I'd been reading all this time, or the dreams I'd been dreaming.

It was difficult keeping my excitement to myself, even from my seat at the back, as we took off into a clear blue sky.

The turbulence started about half way. Out of the window on my left the big black cumulus clouds in the distance looked ominous. Why wasn't the pilot turning to the right?

But across the plane out of the right-hand windows the clouds were exactly the same. There would be no escaping the storm. My body tensed with excitement.

Bright flashes exploded the sky, blindingly near. Every so often there was a loud crack. The noise of thunder was drowned out by the engines and screaming women. The lights came on.

The seat belt command was too late for the stewardess in the deep blue sari. I watched, incredulous, as she suddenly became airborne, hit the roof and fell down. We had struck an enormous down draught. No one could get up to help her at first in that chaos - tossing and banging and luggage thrown in all directions. She was hurt by flying plates.

Ma kept looking back at me, trying to seem unconcerned.

"Are you all right, Toon?"

"Yes, I'm fine, Ma."

She looked uneasily at my big happy smile. Baba just sat there at the front, his face hidden.

I was sorry for the stewardess and the terrified passengers, but how could I not feel exhilarated?

When we burst into blue sky again and the turbulence stopped, surely they appreciated how awesome and thrilling it had been.

What would it be like to fly a course through all that turmoil and land safely after all? The pilot must feel like god.

The nearest I could get to this feeling, a very pale reflection of it, was sitting behind the wheel of a car.

My ability to drive made the holiday in Kashmir possible. Kashmir, with its stunning hilly scenery, was my idea. None of my four friends drove, but they had the money which I lacked.

"I'll get us a car," I said. "And fettle it. I'll act as driver and mechanic in lieu of my share."

Kashmir was 1600 miles from Calcutta.

We hired a houseboat with a cook and servant, on Dal Lake, near Srinagar. We'd been on board sipping beer in the evening, listening to reports of Queen Elizabeth's Coronation when the news first broke.

Sherpa Tensing and Sir Edmund Hillary had reached the summit of Everest on the 29th May.

En route for Kashmir

We were fascinated. Imagine their struggles. Imagine what they felt like with the whole world beneath them, knowing they had achieved their impossible aim. We drank more beer. We drank to Hillary and Tensing. We drank to the Queen.

"Let's go into the *shikara*," said Somi Das.

The little gondola-like boat for paddling between the houseboat and the shore was attached to the side. It was three feet or so down the houseboat steps to the water - Kutu Das was coming down, ready to jump into the narrow boat.

Somi Das was playing the fool. He pulled it away as Kutu jumped and Kutu fell into the water. We all laughed. Nobody realized he couldn't swim. We waited for his head to re-appear.

"My God, he's drowning. *Tara tari*! Quick," I shouted.

Nobody moved.

There were no demons in the water but tall grasses to entangle and snare. I seemed to be caught, held down below the surface. Must not panic. Help me, Lord Shiva. I grabbed Kutu under the water. He was unconscious. Had he knocked his head against the boat or had I knocked him? No Jethaamoni to rescue us here. Pull away from the weeds, an effort, suddenly free - and air.

Kutu, safe, recovered. In his face, briefly, the features of Ahmed. Was this a kind of vindication? But for Ahmed everything finished in the Ganges in Patna all those years ago. He would never sip beer.

My pocket diary was soaked and the ink was running. The excitement had gone and a sort of agitation took its place.

There was Hillary at the top of his mountain. How great he must feel. And here was I still waiting - for what? Until the time was right? It was like waiting for the rains to start. They had to come sometime, when the gods chose - you couldn't hurry them. But the tension built up inside and you couldn't wait to be soaked.

How much longer could I bide my time?

CHAPTER 10

The 1954 Table-Tennis World Championships were to take place in Wembley, England. Would I like to go as second reserve?

It was fitting that it should be the strong uncle, who had survived prison and torture to arrive at our door back in Allahabad, who was planning to help me break free. He was going to pay my fare and had secured an apprenticeship training for me in London with the engineering firm of Taylor Woodrow. My passport was ready. The time had come.

"No," said Baba. "He can't go. I can't allow him to go."

And that was that.

Baba got me a job as salesman with Underwood Typewriters and Calculating Machines in Mango Lane, Calcutta, starting on 12th March 1954. I vowed that I would get out, somehow or other, within a year.

My restlessness increased. How could I prove myself, prepare myself? Ma and Baba gave permission for my visit to relatives in Allahabad. They thought I was taking the train.

It took eight days to cycle there, half way across India on poor roads, sweating with the tremendous heat and the effort. On the tenth day I returned home triumphant with the bicycle on the train and no-one was any the wiser.

Mr Banerjee, Uncle's great friend, had left Calcutta in 1926 on a bicycle. He returned in 1938, on a bicycle. He'd used buses in the cities but had cycled all over the world. His book was by my bed, thumbed and worn. How much he had seen, how much he had learnt. And in Holland he had been taught to fly.

I didn't have money like Mr Banerjee, but that was what I was going to do, however long it took.

The monsoon was nearly two weeks late and the heat was unbearable. In the villages women would be praying to the images of gods they'd created on the barren fields, looking anxiously up at a hazy sky.

Calcutta, too, longed for cooling rain as the heat and tension mounted. At the YMCA on the Chowringhee, after a hard game of table-tennis with Saroj, the sweat was running down my legs and soaking my socks and tennis shoes. I needed another drink, a cool *nimbu pani* this time - fresh limewater with salt and pepper.

Outside the sky above the Maidan was filled with black billowing clouds, huge and menacing. Tremendous forks of lightning flashed. Thunder boomed. The women in the fields would be rejoicing - their rice could be planted.

To the south-east the white Victoria Memorial had turned to dark grey. To the west the Red Road, wartime runway for the Hurricanes and Spitfires, had disappeared behind a curtain of rain. The curtain was advancing at great speed.

Already a few large drops of rain fell on me, the pavement started to steam and the wind got up. I began to shiver. I ran past the Tiger Cinema towards the *paan* shop for my lime drink. Between the cinema and the shop was the modern frontage of Austin Brothers Sales Office.

There were Vespa scooters, new to India, in the showroom window. It was the first time I'd seen them displayed. I never reached the *paan* shop.

I stood very still in front of the lit showroom. The wind, gale force by now, was trying to lift me off my feet but I didn't care. I stared fascinated at the cyclops eye lamp on the front mudguard, the wide front apron, the tiny neat wheels and the running board. Plenty of places to put luggage and ample room for two on the bench seat. Wouldn't this be better than a bicycle? And if there were two of us ...

I found myself looking thoughtfully at each of my friends in turn, and at the other table-tennis players.

Being number four in Bengal by now and a top class doubles player brought me into contact with interesting people of different nationalities. There was so much world to see outside India. And it would be an easier matter once the escape was made and my confidence boosted, to learn to fly.

I sauntered past the showroom again. One of the brothers who owned the garage happened to be around. He was enthusiastic about the new Vespas.

"You've got a second-hand one there too, I see."

"Yes," he said. "A bargain. It belonged to the Maharaja of Nandgaon. You know what they're like for having the first of everything imported. This Maharaja bought it for his wife but she fell off while she was learning and hurt herself a little - not much. She bent the handlebar and did some other minor damage. The Maharaja got cross and asked for it back. Then he returned it to the garage."

"Supposing," I said. "I were to undertake a world trip on it. Would there be any concession on the price?"

He laughed. "I'm afraid not. It's already half price. But the longest and best trip on a Vespa every year draws a prize, if you finish up at Genoa. How about it?"

"I'll give it some thought," I said, and we both laughed.

How about it? I knew I would be capable of undertaking such a journey, but there was the question of money, a friend to share the challenge and most difficult of all, permission from Ma and Baba.

Selling typewriters was not exactly stimulating but it did earn money. I stepped up my rather unorthodox methods of increasing sales, blackmailing and bribing with my only asset available for barter - table-tennis coaching.

"How about buying six typewriters? Remember I'm teaching your wife to play table-tennis ... Two? She might not get to play that well ... OK, three."

The yogi had been right, I couldn't leave it all to God.

After the six months, my old eating habits had gradually crept back and my asthma sometimes reappeared but basically I was still fit and I would need to stay that way.

I started mentioning my idea to one or two rich friends. They seemed keen. Surely one of them would want to travel round the world on a scooter with me.

"You must give me five years, Ma. Then I can educate myself."

My only hope would be to wear her down with all the arguments I could think of. If she were to give her permission, Baba would have to stand by it. She would be far easier to work on than Baba.

"I need to get away from Calcutta, Ma. To experience life. My spirit ..."

I thought I was beginning to get somewhere. Then it all came out. It was the horoscope of course. It had been the horoscope all along.

"After this child grows to manhood he will marry somebody from across the *kala pani*, the dark waters, in England...

He will travel a lot and live abroad...

His profession will have something to do with electricity...

He will have a serious accident..."

"This is why your father doesn't want you to fly. You don't know how much your father loves you."

So this was the terrible mystery, locked in the almirah on ten feet of scrolled parchment. It was Baba who'd made the connection between electricity and flying. We had electricity here in Calcutta although it was often cut off, especially during the monsoon, and Ma used a coal fire to cook by. But in the villages the only electricity was in the sky, in the storms.

Suppose Baba was right and the predictions really were about flying? That was an exciting thought. And if the accident applied to flying? Frightening, in a thrilling sort of way. Not as disturbing as Baba's dark angry eyes. Once away from them, threatening horoscopes could be forgotten.

Then there was the bit about living abroad. Obviously they hadn't wanted to plant the idea in my head. But it was already there.

As for marrying an English girl, that was total rubbish. The Fathers in St Xavier's at Patna had found penfriends in America for us and some of the girls had sent photographs. We were fascinated by their white skin, "Look they've got freckles," and we used to examine their handwriting with awe. Of course I'd met white people since, especially through table-tennis, and enjoyed their company, but as for marrying one of them - it was just unthinkable.

I left Ma alone for a few days. If she thought she had frightened me off my resolve, she was mistaken. Either it was rubbish or it was going to happen anyway. And if flying really was involved the sooner I got going the better.

As for Baba, if he loved me so much, why didn't he talk to me? I couldn't do anything right anyway. Ma said he would treat me like an adult if I were responsible and studied, then he could give me a job in the railways. I didn't want a job in the railways. I wanted to fly. "*Urbo*. Get airborne," insisted the voice.

The gods understood. My continued prayers and offerings of marigolds and rice to Kali and to Shiva were not ignored. My spirit was always uplifted. Indra the god of thunder, lightning and rain also received my homage.

"Just give me five years, Ma."

"*Acha*. All right. As long as you come back again."

She was very busy and I had worn her down. She didn't know that the journey would be made on a little scooter. She didn't imagine that I would ever actually organize myself to go.

I bought the Maharaja's Vespa, four months after the conversation in the showroom, and hid it at a friend's house. Now it was mine at last I could hardly bear to part with it. Preparations began in earnest.

And one by one my rich friends let me down - keen until the last minute, then sorry, no.

Ma had studied all the effects of the moon and sun and planets in the Panjika. The most auspicious dates for departure turned out to be 30th January, 28th February and 12th March. So if I really were to leave early the next year, 1955, it had to be on one of those dates. If I really were to leave? Was it still a game to her?

Sheila knew all my most private plans from the beginning. We understood each other.

"I'm so happy for you, *Chot'da*. You are right to get away."

With her long dark hair and beautiful eyes Sheila was the darling of the family. But for how long? She had fallen deeply in love, with a poor music teacher. And he was a Christian.

"Ma and Baba will make trouble, Sheila."

"I don't care."

"Good luck to you, my little sister."

There was nothing I could do to help her then. I had to work on my own escape first.

The scooter and I would have to get to know each other quickly and secretly. It was December and the weather was pleasantly cool. I was going to visit Uncle's friend near Hazaribagh - by train the family assumed. This was about half the distance of my bicycle trip but the road was very rough and it was dark as I searched for the house. The journey had gone well so far, the scooter felt right and my spirits were high. It would be a good idea to test how easy it was to ride by moonlight in case the lights failed on the journey.

The dark red earth, the shadows of mango trees across the moon, the scooter scudding slowly through the silence. The bamboo barrier across the road to stop the lorries at night - I saw it too late.

The bamboo caught the left side of my forehead and I fell off.

There was only a small dent in the scooter, but it taught me a lesson. Uncle's friend agreed not to mention the scooter to my family and the return journey was uneventful. Five hundred kilometres clocked up.

"I'll come with you."

Nitish Biswas, my table-tennis partner, ranked fifth in Bengal, to my fourth. His back problem needed treatment in London but he had no means of getting there. With my skill in massage, learnt in Patna, I could help relieve the pain on the journey but how would he feel about a scooter? He saw the little Vespa and was still game, although he worried about money.

"Ask your father. He must be very wealthy."

"You must be joking." Begging from Baba was out of the question.

We would live from hand to mouth, I said, play exhibition matches and sell our story as we went along.

We made a vow that if either of us got into difficulties or were ill, the other would carry on. Neither of us would have to abandon the trip for the other.

We could not be ready earlier than Ma's last date, 12th March. Any later and it would be too hot to cross the desert, too late for Utrecht where we hoped to attend the table-tennis championships and too late to pick up the prize in Genoa.

Baba read the local newspaper from cover to cover so he must have seen the articles about us in the two months before we left. But he never commented, and neither he nor Ma asked any questions.

Two well known table-tennis stars of Bengal with an urge to see people and places were embarking on a round-the-world tour on a 125 cc motor scooter, he must have read. They were to take five years and then Toon Ghose would write a book about their travels.

That aspiration would be sufficient later on to turn me into a "literature student", and Nitish, who worked in medical supplies, would become a "medical student". We reckoned that being students would open a few doors on our trip.

There was no need to mention the deeper urge to get away, to spread my wings and taste freedom, to give myself enough confidence and courage to put aside Baba's angry eyes and achieve what I wanted, to fly.

March 12th was getting nearer. The scooter was being prepared. I'd designed a canvas bag round a tubular frame for carrying fresh water - essential for travelling through deserts - and a big canvas box to attach to the apron at the front. We had a spare can of petrol, our bedding to be strapped onto the running board, then there was the stove, our clothes ...

March 3rd, the Holi Festival. Ma and Baba would have to be told, face to face. I went to their room, heart beating. Anticlimax. They still didn't really catch on, still hoped I wouldn't go.

You could lose yourself in the fun of the Holi Festival. Sheila and Dada and I went round to the relatives in turn, armed with dry powders in scarlet, green, sky-blue and yellow to smear on laughing foreheads, rainbowed in return. Then out came syringes with coloured water to squirt at each other. The heat was building up and the water cooled us down. We played hard, all day. Several times our eyes met, mine and Sheila's, still brown in our multicoloured faces, met with knowing.

I bought a very fat journeybook with stiff covers to record our progress. We studied the route, Calcutta to London, which the AA sent us. The countries were only names to us. How would all those white people, so much stronger and more powerful than us, react when we arrived? Would we even make it there?

But there could be no question of failure. Whatever happened, we would carry on regardless. And the road must finish up in London - the route said so.

We had to have some cash in hand - there was not much left and not much time. My wrist watch! It was a good one and only two years old.

In the Bow Bazaar Street I could get money for it straight away. Walking absentmindedly through the dark, stinking corridors of the Chorbazaar, Thieves' Market, I came across a watch shop. How many of these grand old grandfather clocks and ladies' bejewelled wrist watches were genuine, I wondered.

The shopkeeper quickly produced a watch. "It's good, you know," he said with an honest smile. "It keeps excellent time - guaranteed. You'll like it. It's going for one tenth of the standard price - just ten rupees."

"No, I can't afford to buy. I've come to sell my watch. It's a similar one."

But the watch was not on my wrist. A terrific thump in my heart. Surely I couldn't have dropped it?

I took the watch he'd produced. Yes, it was mine.

"It's mine, you thief."

"*Aastay, aastay*, my fine Sahib, slowly, slowly. Have it. It's all yours for ten rupees. I'm almost giving it to you free." His honest smile was confident.

Useless to argue. I calmed down and told him, as friend to friend, about our world trip and how poor we were. I would have practically nothing on me, if he took away my watch and sold it back to me, I said. He looked at me long and closely, as if trying to determine my integrity.

At last he spoke. He told me in strict confidence that he had been on my heels long before I entered his shop. He wouldn't have been so successful if I hadn't been so unmindful.

"This is a good lesson for a future world tourist. Let's not argue. Since we are both poor, you give me five rupees and I give you back your watch. If you had been an ordinary man and not a world tourist I'd have given it back free. You understand? Stealing openly like this is an art, not a crime."

His dark brown eyes glittered in the lamp light and his smile was triumphant as he took the five rupees and handed back my watch. A great man. Perhaps the lesson was more useful than the money after all. Were we that desperate? I would keep the watch as a kind of security.

CHAPTER 11

Ma had to believe now that I was actually leaving. Nothing was going to stop me. I dared not look into her beautiful face and dark eyes, normally so calm.

"*Ahmar kopal kee hollo?*" she wailed. "Why has fate dealt me this blow?"

I stuck a photograph of her in the front of my journeybook, opposite a postcard of Gandhi. At the back of the book I copied out songs to God and inspiring poems of Tagore, in Bengali.

Ma

A few days before we were to leave, Baba got his longed-for promotion, Chief Commercial Superintendent.

"It doesn't mean so much, in this time of sadness because you are leaving, Toon."

No emotional blackmail would deter me now.

Ma bowed to the inevitable and arranged for the Brahmin priest to come and give us his blessing.

Ma's little prayer room doubled as a storeroom where she kept her rice and dhal and fruit. The priest sat in here, with Nitish and me squeezed together in front of him. He chanted prayers and blessed us and smeared red paste on our foreheads. Ma watched, smiling.

The priest hadn't finished.

"I've never blessed a vehicle before," he confessed with a sparkle in his eyes. "But this scooter will be part of your body and soul by the time you've finished your journey."

In the bedroom Dada and I shared, the Vespa stood ready on its stand. The priest blessed it and smeared red paste on the handlebars. We were ready to go.

"You are not ready yet," said Ma. "I need to give you more things."

"We've got enough already, Ma. We've got a stove, we've got blankets, we've got underclothes, tee-shirts ... We've got food, my mouth organ ... In any case we have to leave on the 12th. You said so yourself."

"Yes, you must start your journey on the 12th. But you could go round to the Pannadas' house and sleep the night there so that we could all eat together on Sunday and then you could go."

She had it all worked out. It seemed churlish to deny her one last day.

"So I go out and turn right, then right again, and it's three or four houses up."

"No, you must turn left and go a different way round so that you are out of sight of our house."

So on the 12th, exactly one year after starting my job in Mango Lane - I'd managed to keep my vow, just - I turned left out of 85B Lansdowne Road, and took about a mile's diversion to arrive at the Pannadas' house in Hazra Road.

We ate together on the 13th, Ma crying in spurts and then recovering.

"*Takur kee korlen*? What has God done to me?"

About 600 well-wishers were gathered with the press photographers in the Pannadas' large courtyard in front of the white louvred doors and pink steps. They filled the courtyard and spilled out onto the street.

Sheila wasn't there - we'd said our private goodbyes and the sweet sound of her sitar still echoed in my head. The scooter waited on its stand, with Nitish beside it. Garlands of marigolds were thrown around our necks over our white shirts. I bowed down, time after time, to touch the feet of my elders and receive their blessing, Ma last of all.

"Thou art the ruler of the minds of all people
dispenser of India's destiny
Thy name rouses the hearts of Punjab, Sind, Gujarat and Maratha
Of the Dravida and Orissa and Bengal."

When I saw all those well-wishers and they started to sing the National Anthem I thought my heart would burst.

"It echoes in the hills of the Vindyas and Himalayas
mingles in the music of Jamuna and Ganges
and is chanted by the waves of the Indian Sea ..."

As the scooter sprang into life a tremendous cheer went up and everyone started to clap.

"*Shuva Jatri. Bon Voyage ...*"

Behind us, a heart-rending yell as Ma fell to the floor.

I knew she would recover and that time would heal. I knew I mustn't look back at her or I might not find the courage to continue. I rode on.

The relief was overpowering. It was a tremendous feeling. I was free. And so hard and powerful somehow because I couldn't feel the pain like Ma, and there was no guilt, just an incredible lift.

I had broken the power Ma and Baba had over my life without totally disobeying them. For that moment in time

I became indestructible. Like India I had gained my independence.

Some of our friends followed us by car to the other side of Howrah station, over the bridge, for a final goodbye. Did the change show on my face? My spirits were high. We were starting on a never-ending quest. Our aim was not *shona*, gold or any concrete goal which would disappear once achieved, but something spiritual, indefinable, which would stay with us for ever. I wished all the world could share in my exhilaration.

We rode straight to the Tarokeshwar temple, 14 or so miles out of Calcutta and prayed to Lord Shiva. Lord Shiva could drink poison and survive - that was why he was often portrayed blue. The snake wound itself round his neck while he smoked his opium. This God would protect us through all danger. He would be up there, a spiritual being somewhere in a vast sky that covered every land, and yet he was a God I could relate to in human terms, and a forgiving God.

Help us to surmount all the obstacles and carry out this journey, I whispered. Travel with us.

Because I knew that, as for my country, gaining independence was only the beginning.

CHAPTER 12

Pakistan, Iran, Iraq, Syria, Turkey, Greece, Yugoslavia - place names rang in my head like mantras. Italy, Austria, Switzerland, Germany, France, England - imagined scenes rolled behind my eyes.

But the first stage was to cross the vastness of Northern India from Calcutta in the east to Amritsar in the west. Thirteen hundred miles.

We took the road through Durgapur, stopping the first night at Asansol with relatives.

"Why do you have to leave so early?"

A little crowd gathered. Impatient to go, we sat proudly on the scooter, hemmed in by rolls of bedding, petrol can, canvas water bag, stove, bundles of clothes and the big canvas box jutting from the apron at the front. The scooter was already starting to feel like home.

A little roar and we were off. The going got harder as we rode towards Benares and Allahabad, but it was still so flat and familiar. I'd been this way countless times - as an end in itself, not the prelude to a journey far more thrilling. We wanted to finish with the familiar - hearing the same language, feeling the same dust and heat, seeing the same palm trees, mango trees, bullock carts, bicycles, graceful women with their heads piled high, cows and goats crossing our path to scatter just in time, the occasional lorry belching black fumes. God, there would be miles and miles like this.

England was so far off, another world. Everything would be clean there. The roads would be of new asphalt with surfaces so highly polished we'd be able to see our faces in them. Nothing like these dirty treacherous roads. Europeans, stronger and more powerful, would be able to do things better than we could. They'd all have jobs, spend their free time playing games and visiting nice places. Their affluence would make them easy-going, confident. The buildings would be magnificent - clean and perfectly maintained... And the church bells would ring.

I wanted to see the big church on the roundabout in Allahabad, whose bells rang out on my way to school. It would be a foretaste of things to come. But although we'd been riding hard and our legs were stiff, by the second night we weren't anywhere near Allahabad.

"It's no good. We'll have to stop here."

Travellers could sleep near one of the filthy tea houses free of charge. We found the energy to drag our tarpaulin off the scooter and lay it out on the floor at the roadside. In the morning there would be tea to drink and some sort of breakfast.

The mosquitoes were unbelievably vicious that night. In my dream there were so many of them that they literally lifted me off the floor. I was almost flying with them. They dropped me as I woke, my skin covered in bites. It was cold in the early morning, colder than in Calcutta - this was the centre of India, well away from the sea. As it was also hotter - very hot - during the day, we set off early in the morning.

"*Chai*?"

Sipping the morning tea with my eyes closed banished the dirty surroundings and bathed me in the lovely scent of flowers and unleavened bread. I tried to keep that scent with me for as long as possible.

At about midday the heat started to bite. The surface of the rough Tarmac road was melting in parts and tracks could be seen in it where cars had passed. This was the road I'd followed on my bicycle months before, sweating with the heat and effort. We weren't so badly off on the scooter - fast enough for the breeze to cool us - but when we stopped ...

The temperature was something like 45°C. Some of the wayside villages with their mud huts were cooler. We would hang around until the heat was less fierce, drinking tea from little terracotta pots.

The food was different here. There wasn't as much rice in Bihar, but more gram flour, made from chick peas. Mixed with water and kneaded together with spices this flour made my favourite *sattu*, cheap, nourishing and delicious with chutney.

Our road continued, roughly north-west, past Kanpur and Agra towards Delhi.

At night the traffic increased, with trucks carrying spices, cement or foodstuffs - old trucks whose engines couldn't withstand the heat of the day. Roadside teahouses stayed open 24 hours, so we were able to start at four in the morning with food inside us and cover some distance in the cool. The sun rose and set at six.

My frustration with familiar sights was mounting - I'd travelled even on this road three or four times already. I felt so high, geared to tackle anything that came our way.

But there was nothing more challenging here than mosquitoes. Just hot, hard riding.

Dreams of England, prayers to Lord Shiva and the problems of other vehicles relieved the monotony. When one of the old trucks broke down, mechanics would appear on the scene from nowhere and cobble something as the missing part - they couldn't afford to buy anything new.

"Watch out. Another one."

A line of broken bricks placed round it warned that a truck was out of action and we had to swerve past the mechanics with their heads stuck under the bonnet.

When we reached Delhi on the sixth day every inch of our skin was covered in mosquito bites and every muscle in our bodies ached like hell. Nitish had only ridden pillion but he had to contend with the pain from his back. Extremes of temperature, lack of sleep and the bites had taken their toll on us both. Nitish had a high fever. To feel so bad when we hadn't even left India ...

Bhandari, a table-tennis coach, welcomed us into his home in Delhi. We made such an incredible recovery that on the fourth evening we played an exhibition match.

Our stay in the capital was longer than we'd have liked - visas for 13 countries had to be obtained.

It was a waiting time. The heat was stifling. I wandered round the big ring of little shops and stalls in Connaught Place and acquired a box camera for 14 rupees. I bought a khaki solar hat for the deserts, a balaclava for the cold and some very handsome tiger skin gloves.

As I stroked the markings on the gloves, the tiger's eyes flashed on my mind, the tiger's eyes caught in the headlights of Baba's car on the Durgapur forest road. Yes, I was taking up the challenge now, all right. The road was mine. Better to think of that than Baba's angry eyes.

Always on the lookout for foreign registration plates in Delhi, an Austin Devon in a garage caught our attention.

I questioned the driver with his white beard and Muslim cap.

"This is Memsahib's car. She's travelling from Malaya to England."

The driver pointed out a young lady paying for petrol. Apparently she'd hired him only while she was in Delhi.

"Excuse me, Madam," I said. "I believe you're going to London by road. So are we."

Pamela was small and vibrant with an open smile, rosy cheeks and big deep blue eyes that matched her frock. She was travelling on her own in the Austin Devon from Malaya, where her father owned a rubber plantation, to Oxford to get married.

"You are? What kind of car have you got?"

"We're going in that." I pointed to our little Vespa waiting beside Nitish.

Pamela burst out laughing.

"You're joking. You'll never get there in that."

"Yes, we will."

I met Pamela later at the YMCA to compare routes. Nitish and I had originally opted to follow the route based on the old caravan trails passing through Peshawar and Kabul, but realized we'd have to take the alternative route the AA had given us because of fighting on the Afghanistan/Pakistan border. The war had started that month.

"I'm going via Afghanistan," said Pamela.

"You can't. There's a war."

"I won't have any problems getting through. I've got a British passport."

"I've a feeling we'll meet again," I said. "There's really only one road to London."

"Oh no. My father has so many friends in Afghanistan. I'll get through."

Her eyes flashed so I didn't insist, but the strong hunch that our paths would cross remained. We wished each other good luck.

Once the visas were ready we left Delhi, on the scooter which gave Pamela such amusement, for Amritsar, north west through the Punjab. We'd be crossing over to Pakistan too far south for a last look at Kashmir, the India I loved the most.

As we neared Amritsar and the border, 1300 miles into our journey, a real sense of achievement elated us. My body tensed with anticipation and my head felt light and clear. Breath came freely. The challenge we'd so longed for was within reach. The desert beckoned.

We wanted to travel as light as possible, so we started shedding our spare clothes, offering them to the poor. Any more unwanted clothes we gave away at the temple in Amritsar.

It was the stove that took up all the space and each time it was used it had to be unpacked and packed up again in its box. Why were we keeping this nuisance when we'd managed to get good food all across India? We kicked it away - and nearly set fire to the woods by the road.

CHAPTER 13

The border. A very positive looking barrier with stern uniformed guards. What would the Pakistani Muslims think of us Hindus? Accounts of past incidents exploded in my mind and I thought it quite likely these men would chop off our heads. Nitish too was worried.

We crossed over with thumping hearts. Nothing happened.

The other side was not so different from our own - barren, dusty, with the occasional familiar mango, neem or banyan tree. Our first stop was Lahore, a beautiful garden city where peacocks roosted in the trees and a signpost pointed two ways. To the left: "London via Quetta 6,332 miles" and to the right: "London via Kabul 6,886 miles".

It would have to be the left fork, avoiding Afghanistan. A 500 mile short cut after all!

"Are the roads all right?"

"*Bahoot acha rasta*. Very good roads."

They were so cut up we often couldn't ride. In the worst places we struggled hour after hot hour to cover a few miles. But we were on our way. India was behind us and everywhere else waited ahead.

Multan, half way between Lahore and Quetta, was dry and dusty. We reached the small railway station late in the evening and made for the cycle stand.

"Yes, I'll watch over your scooter."

Rahim had kind brown eyes, a black beard and most of his black hair - just one light coloured patch of skin showing through in stark contrast. His clothes, a long shirt down to his knees and loose trousers, were as dirty and dusty as everything else in the station. He saw our tired faces.

"Have a bed."

He was on duty for the entire night, watching over the scooter as well as the cycles, while Nitish and I slept soundly in his cot. He would be the first person outside India to write in my journeybook.

Only he couldn't write. So I wrote for him and he gladly penned his signature, like a little fish caught in weeds. He wished us a good journey.

We were riding through a strange land now. Nothing but sand mounds and camels and dry, dry heat. Even the cawing crows sounded as though their throats were parched. But I wasn't complaining. I'd never seen anything like it and was totally enthralled.

Nobody else existed in this barren land. We were on our own. Nitish, his back giving him increasing pain, had learnt to fall asleep with his head against my back as he clutched me round the waist.

I was alone with myself, silent but for the scooter, free as Chil the kite circling above us in the blue-grey, cloudless sky, a sky that knew no boundaries, but whose immensity enclosed us all. My breath came freely and easily. There was such power inside me that nothing could possibly go wrong. Gods or no gods, I was invulnerable. I felt ready to conquer the world.

The last travellers at the Baluchistan/Pakistan border had passed two months before. A no-man's land, formidable, barren, rocky, hilly, full of stray camels. The stalwart guard spoke Baluchi and a little Urdu. He carried a gun on a strap over his shoulder and a band of bullets round his waist on top of his pyjama-like Kabuli dress, but the wrinkled reddish-brown face beneath the tight turban was not unkind.

Everyone at Bewater Post was pleased to see strangers. We talked into the night. Someone played a sarangi and I got out my mouth organ. The music drew us together, then lost itself in the eerie darkness beyond.

The border behind us, the road was no more than a worn path through the stark landscape - so beautiful and so raw it seemed that no other form of life could exist. We came across a pass, one side steep mountains, the other side sheer drop. After six miles or so of climbing we began to hear noises - not the purr of the scooter coming back to us in an echo, we'd become used to that. These were different noises, and cries.

We both saw the man herding his camels across the pass - about 500 of them - hold up his hands in horror. And we both immediately understood. If we'd tried to go through we would have scattered all these animals and they would have fallen over the side to their death. So we stopped the engine and waited for them to pass. Two hours.

"Tik, tik. It's OK."

The camel herdsman greeted us in Urdu before we rode on.

A new hazard presented itself now - there was no avoiding the flints. They were everywhere and it was only a matter of time before we had a puncture. Down in a valley we hit a flint and the rear tyre burst. The noon sun beat furiously on our new solar hats as we squatted on the path to repair it.

We'd already noticed four turbaned men with their guns on top of the hill. As soon as we stopped they started approaching, ferocious, magnificent, with ruddy brown unsmiling faces beneath their white turbans.

"I hope they're not bandits." Nitish was apprehensive.

We'd heard about the bandits in this area.

"We've got nothing to offer so we'll be all right."

They stood in front of us. One of them could speak a little Urdu. His voice was loud and deep.

"*Pinay ko pani?* You got water?"

"Yes, of course."

They started drinking, carelessly, as if water was as plentiful as sand. All the muscles in my body tensed.

"No!" Nitish touched one of them on the shoulder.

"Don't be stupid," I hissed in Bengali. "Just be quiet."

We had to let them drink otherwise we would be beaten up. At least there was more fresh water in the carrier inside the front box. Please God they wouldn't find that.

As if reading my thoughts, the tallest bandit took out a knife and slashed open the box, exposing our canvas water container. A dreadful throbbing began in my head. They were going to take the one thing we couldn't do without.

"No!" Nitish again.

They turned on him this time and dealt him a couple of vicious kicks up his backside, watching coldly as he fell groaning in pain.

Appeal to them?   Pointless. They would probably have finished us off there and then.

"*Shu Krya*. Thank you," I said. "How far is the next village?"

"A hundred and fifty kilometres."

They spitefully scattered all our belongings over the flinty ground and made off, still clutching the precious water container.

Silence. Nitish sat up, painfully. We looked at each other. One hundred and fifty kilometres in this beautiful hostile place with no water? One hundred and fifty kilometres of scorching day and bitter night?

We looked at the scooter. It had a pathetically fragile air, stripped of its load, alone in that immense, barren landscape.

I shook myself. We had a long journey ahead, and the sooner I began packing up the scooter the better. They'd at least left the petrol can. Perhaps the roads would improve soon. Somehow we would get to the next village - and water.

Water! The most wonderful gift on earth. By the following day we would have given anything for just one sip. How long could we survive without water? If anything should happen would Ma ever forgive me?

"*Takur kee korlen?*" she would wail. "What has God done to me?"

"I told you - it was all in the horoscope," Baba would say.

Lord Shiva, send us water.

As if in answer to our prayers, a village shimmered ahead of us - trees and buildings, and surely water. God had not deserted us. Parched tongues hanging from our mouths, we tried to summon the energy to reach the village.

But it disappeared, like all the other mirages and hallucinations - villages, trees, camels, people, wells, even a truck. We stopped the scooter, gasping for breath again, stumbling, losing our balance, drained of all energy. How much longer could we endure this torture? How long could we survive without water?

Something deep inside seemed to be pushing us onwards. We would get there. We chewed again on our shirt buttons - that got the saliva going a bit. Were the gods looking down on us? How small and unimportant we were in all this vastness.

Thought was coming in disconnected fragments. Keep going. No birds. Only sandflies hunting in packs of three or four. Afternoon.

Another village - stone huts with low roofs wavering through our heat-distorted vision - try not to get excited, we've seen it all before. But there was something different about this village - it did not disappear.

A deep well. After over 24 hours without water it was almost too incredible to be true.

"Don't start drinking too rapidly, otherwise you'll get stomach cramp," I whispered to Nitish, I who wanted to drink and drink and drink.

The first sips were stunning, the most wonderful sensation of my life. Relief, blessed relief.

Mukhtiar

We'd arrived at the small village of Mukhtiar, host to passing camel caravans and trucks. Hospitality was splendid. The chief man took us to the mosque, where one wing, with the most beautiful carpet on the floor, was set aside for travellers to spend the night. After feasting on roast camel we returned to this huge room with the stone roof and lay on the beautiful carpet to sleep. In the corner Muslims knelt and prayed while Nitish and I fell into a wonderful, deep sleep.

It took two days to get from Mukhtiar to Quetta. Nitish had not recovered from the attentions of the bandits and the cramps through drinking too quickly. We rode in silence and arrived at noon.

A few hills had appeared in the distance under the hazy grey sky, but Quetta was sandy, flat, spread out. The houses shook, we were told, but didn't fall down - the frequent earthquakes were anticipated. We had an introduction here, a headmistress, relation of a Christian boy I knew in India through playing table-tennis. Her husband overheard me in the bazaar asking for their house.

A rest and a cup of tea, then it was straight to the only garage to get the scooter serviced. I couldn't miss the Austin Devon. Pamela's car was jacked up with a note on the windscreen, "Toon and Nitish please come and see me."

Was this Pamela, with the sunken cheeks and wild, gaunt look? Only the deep blue eyes, even more striking in her white pinched face, reminded us of the bright young woman we'd met in Delhi.

She too had been attacked by bandits. Then she'd arrived at the Afghanistan/Pakistan border only to be sent back again, 1000 miles. She was injecting herself with drugs to keep calm. I had a feeling we would see her yet again, but this time I kept my thoughts to myself.

Our hostess was the headmistress of the Women's Training School in Quetta. We stayed with the family for four days, in a strange state of normality. We renewed our expired visas, watched a variety show for the convent school's rebuilding fund, played table-tennis at the Brown Gymkhanna Club, visited the school to answer the children's barrage of questions about our trip, and socialized.

On 15th April, we left Quetta for another stretch of sand and camels. Only 712 miles to Zahidan.

The road, built by the army during the war, followed the railway line from Quetta to Zahidan. A goods train passed every seven days. Every 50 miles there was a hut on the railway line with two or three workers to keep sand off the tracks - otherwise they would have been obliterated by sandstorms. But the road, usually about a hundred yards from the railway line, was not looked after - it was cut up and difficult to negotiate with small wheels. Riding on this was very painful for Nitish.

Every morning I massaged his aching body and every morning memories of Sheila and Dada and me as children walking along Ma's spine - the reason for taking the massage course in Patna - played in my head. What would Ma be doing now?

After two days on this road it was obvious Nitish could not cope. He was having to be tied round me and to the scooter as he was nearly passing out. He could hardly speak and he looked half dead. It was time to remember our vow. If something happened to one of us, the other must carry on alone.

I took him to one of the railway huts. The Muslim workers welcomed us and fed us, glad of our company in their lonely job. One of them, in a brownish turban, could speak Urdu and promised to look after Nitish until transport was found. There wouldn't be any cars, he said, but every three or four days there would be a truck, carrying spices perhaps. Meanwhile Nitish was sitting fairly comfortably on the verandah of the hut.

After two hours, just as I was thinking about setting off again, the workers started sniffing the air. They turned as one man, their short beards pointing towards the east. Something was coming from that direction, they said.

The dust could be seen two miles away. Pamela's car was travelling very fast - more than 30 mph.

When she arrived, she didn't drive into the hut but stayed on the road. I rushed out to her.

"Who have you got there?"

Four tyres were on the roof rack, the back of the car was completely filled with all sorts of rubbish she didn't need for this sort of trip - and next to her in the passenger seat was a tall turbaned man in a white robe.

"Toon, Toon, I'll give anything if you can get him out."
Pamela's frightened blue eyes were pleading with me out of
her white, gaunt face.

"Don't worry. I want you to take Nitish."

"He's walking to Mecca but his feet are very swollen. He
threatened me with my life if I didn't take him. What could
I do? So there he is and he won't move. Oh, Toon."

Communication with the pilgrim was impossible, but I
managed to get him out and sitting with us in the hut. He
didn't know that Nitish was going to take his place, didn't know
what was going on at all. He just sat there.

"Start walking slowly towards the car, Nitish."

When Nitish was half way there, the pilgrim stood up and
spoke. One of the workmen translated for us, "Where is this
man going?"

"He's going to see Memsahib."

Suddenly the pilgrim realized what was happening.

I stood up, took out my knife, pointed it.

"Look, if this guy moves one inch I'll throw this at his heart.
I'm very good with knives."

It was the knife we used for peeling potatoes before we
jettisoned the stove.

I heard the car start but dare not take my eyes off the man.
Sick with terror I kept walking backwards towards the scooter
as the tall pilgrim walked towards me. Please, Lord Shiva,
please let the scooter start first time.

CHAPTER 14

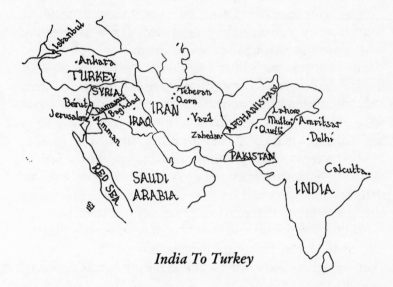

India To Turkey

The scooter did start first time, and during the first mile and a half the road was in good enough condition for a speed of at least 15 mph. I had got away.

But for several days I imagined I could hear him catching up with me on his swollen feet. At night, his tall frame loomed over me, threatening, as I tried to sleep.

The first night on my own I came across an abandoned mosque. The mosque was in ruins and the atmosphere very weird but other people had taken shelter in it - there were black sooty areas where nomads or bedouins had cooked their food. That night, though, there were only the bats. The mosque was full of bats. As darkness fell the worst scenes from Dracula whirled in my head and then I started to hallucinate - bandits with knives and pilgrims with murder in their eyes, and spirits that waited to haunt me all night. It would be impossible to sleep there.

I rode off and slept in the open, two hours away.

The road now was hardly a road at all, just a succession of potholes. No habitation for miles. Nobody. No sign even of the train which was supposed to pass through once a week. This was real desert and I was alone in it, became part of it. I could identify with a single grain of sand. It was frightening, challenging, fascinating. My spirits lifted.

The best time was sunset when the flat sand glowed gold. By day the sky was a hazy greyish blue and mirages of trees and oases shimmered out of the heat. But by night the stars were so bright the sky appeared to be very deep blue. Then the cold dry wind, the *Kandahari Hawa*, showed no mercy.

There were areas where soft sand had blown onto the surface of the road and it was impossible to ride. Walking lost me two or three hours at a time. I still worried about the pilgrim coming after me - alone in that echoing immensity fear stuck.

Eventually the road improved. I could dream again that the scooter and I were flying through the desert. The scooter was like a part of my body by now, just as the priest in Ma's prayer room had predicted. If it broke down I would have to carry it on my shoulders.

In the distance, trees loomed out of the desert. Trees had become familiar to me, alone in all that sand - teasing trees that came and went. But these were not palm trees, more like poplar, and they were real. I was approaching Zahedan.

The trees seemed close but they must have been miles away. They were on a hill and it felt as though I was riding up to a distant castle in a fairy-tale. Still no sign of people.

A little hut and a pole across the road about a mile before Zahedan marked the border with Iran, the Persia of my childhood.

"*Salaam Wallekum.*" I gave the usual Muslim greeting to the customs officer in his blue uniform with gold-coloured buttons and peaked cap.

"*Wallekum Salaam ...*" Then a long string of rapid French. I was allowed to enter Iran.

The sandy-coloured buildings of Zahedan merged with the ground so the trees and the scrubby grass showed up dark, dark green.

The Vice-Consulate seemed the obvious place to make for. Someone else had thought so too.

"Nitish!" I was furious. "What are you doing here? You should be with Pamela."

I was so angry. Luckily for Nitish he was smaller than me - otherwise I would have grabbed him and shaken him to pieces.

"There's no way I'm going to take you - "

"Have you had a look at your face since I left you?" Nitish was staring at me.

I could feel my face cracked with the dry, cold wind but I hadn't realized how much the cracks had bled and that the blood had clotted into my beard of three weeks. I calmed down.

Nitish had insisted Pamela drop him off in Zahedan instead of taking him to Teheran or London. Well, he would have to make his own way to Teheran - there were lorries coming up from Oman carrying spices. He would have to beg a lift. We divided the remaining money in half, which left us with the equivalent of nine pounds each.

I left Zahedan alone at four in the morning on April 25th, 1955. The road was so bad I made almost no progress. I saw nobody.

The bitter *Kandahari Hawa* blew from the mountain ranges in the north and tore my face to pieces. The road was impossible and the hot sun beat down on me as I struggled to make headway. It was hell.

Just before Bam the sand was so soft that wooden boards had been put down to help. But it was still impossible to ride the scooter. I forced myself to struggle on.

After Bam, more than 24 hours since I'd left Zahedan, I seemed to have crossed some sort of threshold, pushed past the limit of endurance.

"What the hell am I doing? Why am I here? Lord Shiva, why are you torturing me like this?" I cried aloud.

"We didn't tell you to travel," said the gods.

"Where am I? What is going on? Why am I crying out for God? Even he has deserted me. If I don't see anybody what is going to happen? Ma!"

"We never said you could fly," said the gods.

"*Chellay, ahmar chellay,*" wailed Ma. "My son, my son."

A big question mark loomed over the sand. Who was I? I was so frightened, I lost my wits completely. "Lord Shiva, help me!"

I awoke to the pungent smell of mustard and spices. Someone had put cold water on my head and I seemed to be sitting propped up between two men in the front of a truck, alive.

The truck drivers, an Armenian with a very suntanned face and red cheeks, and his Iranian mate, said they'd found me 15 minutes earlier unconscious at the side of the road with my scooter.

"Where did he appear from? We haven't seen any transport."

They'd propped me up between them and had even used some of their precious water on me, I seemed in such a bad way.

They'd also loaded the scooter on to the truck. It was roped up on its side seeping petrol through the spice bags beneath it, unwittingly ruining them.

I stayed with the truck drivers all that day and night, travelling two or three hundred kilometres and spoiling my chances of an entry in the Guiness Book of Records - not that I minded, it was good to be alive.

"I am so grateful," I said over and over. "You saved my life."

"No. no."

There must be some spirit there after all, I thought. God was watching over me, otherwise I would be dead.

They dropped me in Yazd, for the last leg to Teheran.

Yazd was still desert, dry with no vegetation, but there was a gradual climb up from then on until I was on high ground, with no sand.

Loose stones were the problem now. As I tried to negotiate them, the Vespa's small wheels threw me off balance. I fell off countless times, each time adding a new wound to the array on my shin. Without the Vespa's running board as a guard, my legs would have been broken many times.

Then there were the punctures, but I could mend those in my sleep now. The scooter's performance was remarkable. Apart from changing plugs and mending punctures it had needed no attention.

I had grown very hardy myself, my asthma had not re-appeared since leaving India, and most of all I felt very powerful, with Lord Shiva behind me, ready to face anything.

The landscape was subtly changing and with it my mood lightened. The world began to feel cool and look green and hilly, the sky to lose its haziness.

Ahead of me was Qom with its Blue Mosque, like a miniature Taj Mahal. Three splendid blue minarets rose against a graphite sky. I hadn't seen anything like that sky and I suddenly experienced a sense of achievement I couldn't have understood before setting off. My breath came easily.

In my imagination the scooter flew again and I pivoted in the sky above the minarets. Later, climbing the hill out of Qom, I was to look back and recognize that view of the Mosque as if the scooter had actually flown above it. But then it was viewed from a different, stationary perspective whereas flying had given me the freedom to circle round.

The sunset at Qom was beautiful. It still filled my mind as I lay down to sleep on the carpet in the huge room set aside for pilgrims near the Mosque. At night the moon threw strong, stark shadows.

After Qom the silence was so deep, so absolute, that the noise of the scooter purring away came back to me in an echo. In the distance I could see some hills and the vegetation was changing. The sky and the desert were beginning to separate themselves, the heat haze disappearing and the sky changing to pure blue.

It was as if I were up in that sky, spreading everywhere, watching myself on the little scooter and seeing how far I had progressed. Learning to fly would come in good time. I had escaped, I was a free person. The gods were pushing me to face different challenges before I finished up in the sky. There was so much wealth in the stark beauty I had ridden through, alone with my scooter and a few worthless belongings. I felt amazingly rich.

At last clouds began to appear and I knew the desert was completely behind me.

Crossing the desert

As soon as I got to the coast, I vowed, I would throw my solar hat as far as possible into the sea and shout praises to Lord Shiva. I knew I would get there.

But for the time being, after so long in India and the desert, I couldn't wait to get to Teheran, where a new exciting world waited. The road climbed up and up.

I arrived late in the day, starving, and found myself in the main square where the students congregated.

"Nitish!"

He was wandering past a statue on its pedestal. He'd stayed in a hotel since he'd been dropped in the city but had run out of money.

Everything was closed today, he said, so we couldn't sell our story until morning.

We sat down and shared the bit of naan bread, onions and salt left on the scooter. Our stomachs were still empty pits.

"Any small change?" We emptied our pockets.

In the shop we looked longingly at the special boiled eggs but they were too expensive. Buying a piece of bread took everything we'd got.

Outside, Nitish seemed to be fingering something.

"What have you got in your pocket, Nitish?"

"A couple of eggs."

"You had no money."

"But you see, we're hungry, aren't we?"

"You must take them back."

"We'll pay the shopkeeper later."

"But you didn't ask. Give them back."

We gave them back and left the shop quickly. The trick was to stay really quiet, so as not to aggravate our hunger. We spent the night huddled up under the shop with the other vagabonds, our stomachs grumbling. It was not warm but it was not too cold either.

"Why don't you ask your father for money?" Nitish had said. "He can afford to give you plenty."

That was out of the question. Besides, tomorrow once we'd sold our story we would have enough again.

I don't need an umbrella, I thought sleepily, and saw Santosh Babu's peaceful jet black eyes.

Santosh Babu lived about 15 miles from Calcutta and worked in the Post Office there five and a half days a week. The rest of his time was spent in reading palms and foreheads and telling stories, like a guru. He lived very modestly and refused any offerings from anybody, treating everyone who came to see him the same, rich or poor. "I enjoy doing what I do and I am helping you all to help myself," he said.

After his stroke, Baba would ask what was going to happen to him and his work. Why doesn't Baba ask him any real questions, I thought to myself as I watched Santosh Babu on his grey blankets in the light of the hurricane lantern. He had a beautiful, gentle face - short hair, a black beard, peaceful jet-black eyes and a lovely smile.

One day I plucked up courage. "Can you tell us some stories about your life?"

"You know, Toon, one day I said to myself, God I might get wet. The monsoon is coming and I must have an umbrella. I sat looking at my lemon tree and decided to sell the lemons in the market. In previous years when the monsoon came I used to say to myself, God I've got no umbrella but it doesn't matter. Only a few drops would fall on me, but it would rain mercilessly when I got home. For ten years I didn't get wet.

So this year I sold my lemons - my son didn't mind - and got six annas for them. I'd seen the umbrella I wanted, for six annas, so went and bought it."

He had been talking deliberately to me but when I looked round everybody else was spellbound. He began laughing at himself.

"Do you know, the clouds were black, thunder exploded. I said to myself, God I'm not worried at all, I've got an umbrella. It started pouring, pitilessly. We had the worst electrical storm for years - and I was completely soaked in spite of having the umbrella."

No, I would never ask Baba for money. I felt Nitish shift in his sleep. Tomorrow we would sell our story.

"You will do a lot of things that not many people know about," Santosh Babu had said. I preferred his predictions to those in my horoscope. "Remember you have a strong right hand. A changeable life, something to do with the earth and the sky. The sun's influence is very strong. You will be quite safe."

Next thing I knew it was morning.

The second evening we visited the Gurdwara, where the Sikhs, of the Hindu-orientated religion, worshipped in their own hall amongst the Muslims and mosques of Teheran. The head man, with his long, long hair and beard, directed us in to the sound of chanting. A statue of the prophet Guru Nanak stood at the end of the spacious, clean hall with its columns and beautiful carpet and lovely incense-filled atmosphere. We enjoyed the Sikh hospitality for two nights.

Then we were on our feet. Our story was in the newspaper. We challenged the Persian team to a Davis Cup type table-tennis competition. That resulted in free hospitality for seven nights in special rooms in the Roosevelt Stadium. The Sports General - everyone seemed to be some kind of General - spoke fluent French. Although few people spoke English, we had a little band of followers by this time and one of them, Alvandi, spoke English very well.

"I'll take you out. I'll explain everything."

We had money now. We were paid for playing and we'd sold our story. Food was displayed on bicycle wheels on the pavement, naan bread and kebabs, especially our favourite *dumba* lamb, never beef.

The *dumba*, like a football where the sheep's tail should be, was cut off and put in an earthen pot with spices. Alvandi showed us the area set aside beneath each house as a kitchen with a wood fire. This kept the living space above warm. At night the ash would be left on the fire, the *dumba* would be chopped up nicely and kept there with a little water. Very tasty.

The food and the girls.

"I would like to marry 60,000 of them," I told Nitish.

This wasn't only because they were so beautiful - I wanted to save them all from their horrible menfolk. They were so badly treated under the Shah of Iran's regime. Now they were torn between the old and new. Under the influence of the foreign queen Soraya, many girls in Teheran wore Western clothes. As they travelled to work in the hundreds of Mercedes-Benz buses, the men made their lives hell, really abusing them.

Why did human beings treat each other the way they did? Why couldn't the men respect the women? I felt extremely frustrated and angry.

"We could be a very powerful race if we could bind together the old and the new," said Alvandi.

As soon as we left Teheran the old traditions re-asserted themselves. These were very orthodox Muslims. The women were heavily veiled - you could see the faces of the married women but not the unmarried ones - and were mainly dressed in black with long skirts.

We had left Teheran before for a couple of days - rode the scooter to Bandar-e-Pahlavi on the Caspian sea for a swim.

But this time we were continuing our journey - next stop Baghdad, Iraq.

Outskirts of Teheran

From Teheran, already high up, we had to climb the Aveh Pass and the Awa Pass, 8400 feet, into the blue, cloudless sky. The clear air was exhilarating - I almost took off. Then all the people I'd met and the experiences I'd had crowded out the flying thoughts, pushed them into the background. I was not ready to fly yet, I had to escape first, to meet people, talk to them, understand them and get to really know myself. That was the first step.

It was hard climbing up and down again. The higher we were the less efficient the scooter's engine became, slowing us down considerably. It was also very cold up there and the road was bad.

But within two or three days we were approaching Baghdad and sweltering heat. It was already very hot as we neared the city and all the road was cut up. Nitish couldn't help because of his back. I pushed the scooter for two hours.

Roses - crimson, white, pink, yellow - in this heat? The parks were full of them. Baghdad was beautiful, with the very wealthy and the desperately poor mingling together and the cooling river Tigris flowing for them all.

We'd got to know about the ashram in Baghdad well before we reached the city. Sharmaji, the leader, invited us in. We felt immediate respect and affection for this Hindu with his walking stick, white "Nehru" hat, white curly beard, nose flattened over his moustache so that his nostrils were invisible, and proud, kind eyes. He had a chapel, not a temple, and helped all Indians whether they were Hindu or not. The ashram was like heaven on earth after the hell of pushing the scooter on my own.

CHAPTER 15

The Trans-Nairan bus route to Damascus or the road to Amman, capital of Jordan?

We decided on Amman, a hot, sticky journey. The Jordanians were generous with everything except what we craved most - they laughed when we asked for a shower.

We got our shower in the RAF camp in Amman, in spite of the shortage of water, and were given cigarettes. Nitish stayed in the camp while I made a detour to Jerusalem.

I saw Jerusalem - from the outside. The Arabs wouldn't let me past the wall. The points burnt out on the scooter and there was nowhere to get parts. It took two weary days to push the scooter back to Amman.

Next stop Damascus, Syria, the Omayad Mosque. We stood in the market outside the 4000-year-old gate of weathered stone, starving. We needed to earn some money.

"Nitish, get your solar hat and keep it ready. I'll spit."

I spat on the dust in a circle to represent the world, talking to myself. "Round the world from Calcutta to Delhi, to Lahore, to Quetta, to Zahedan, to Teheran, to Amman, to Damascus. Then on to Turkey ..."

A crowd started forming.

"Look Nitish, keep your solar hat open like that."

I put a blanket on the spit circle and stood on my head.

"Put that mouth organ in my mouth."

As I played a few notes more people gathered.

Next I stood up and got on the scooter, racing away to one corner of the square, with the clamp on to keep the throttle constant on 30 kilometres an hour. I stood on the running board and tried to keep my balance.

I misjudged. The scooter went straight through the crowd scattering it as I fell off.

"Come on, I'll give you a ride," I said, gesturing.

Perhaps they thought my fall was deliberate. In any case it didn't put them off. I managed to take seven at a time - two other adults and five children.

We had enough money in the solar hat to buy food.

"As soon as we reach the sea," I reminded Nitish, "this hat will be flung away to the sound of my prayers. I've promised."

We hoped we might be offered accommodation at the Embassy where we went to collect our letters.

"Why don't you two lads sleep down the stairs?" said the Ambassador of India to Syria.

We spent the night in the beautiful building on a rug on the white marble floor. In the morning we sold our story to the newspaper and were solvent again.

I hadn't realized there was a country called Lebanon. It was difficult to get used to these little countries whose habits were so different from one another. Vast India had no such borders and sudden changes. Our route took us through Lebanon, before re-entering Syria to continue north to Turkey - but we needed a *carnet de passage*. For this we were kept in confinement at the border for two days, then given permission to stay in Lebanon for a week.

Our YMCA cards proved useful in Beirut.

"Yes, you can borrow a tent and put it up on the beach. It won't cost you anything."

The sea! For someone whose childhood was spent in the centre of India, who hadn't seen the coast until he was a teenager, the sea was always an exciting place. This beach was very clean and the sand oozed round our bare feet and in between our toes. By the time our tent was erected we had made two friends, Hani and Aziz.

But before we could swim and play in the waves with them like a couple of porpoises, there was something important to be done.

They watched as we picked up our solar hats and walked solemnly down to the water's edge. We raised our arms and threw the hats as far as we could, into the Mediterranean.

"*Om Shivaium. Om Shivaium.*" I shouted at the top of my voice. "Lord Shiva be praised."

We were about to run up the beach, laughing and slapping each other round the shoulders, my promise fulfilled. But the bobbing khaki hats started floating back to us. The tide was coming in.

"We'll sort them out," said our new friends.

Hani and Aziz put the hats on their heads, got in one of the wooden rafts, paddled it right out to sea then took off the hats and hurled them into the waves. We never saw them again. The desert phase of our journey was over. We felt fantastic.

But our stomachs were empty. Tomorrow we would have to sell our story again. We'd spent the last of our money on a snack, but where was tonight's meal coming from? The evening was balmy. We wandered away from the beach down a lane flanked on both sides by tall, very old buildings.

"Toon! Nitish!"

Who on earth? We looked back and saw a man in a creamy coloured silk suit and a Mexican hat.

"Don't you recognize me?"

We kept quiet and shook hands.

"Calcutta, after the match?"

"Oh yes, yes. I know."

He'd been in Calcutta on business and seen us playing table-tennis. There'd been a crowd of 3500 but he'd come personally and congratulated us and then taken us for a meal. Now here he was again, this Italian, 5000 miles away, and he was taking us to a big hotel.

"Like this?" We were very dirty and scruffy.

He came between us, put his arms through ours and marched us in.

"Don't worry about your clothes, you are world travellers - and you are my guests."

Beirut was clean, in contrast to the other cities we'd visited. We passed the modern white airport buildings, lit up for the night. One day I would fly, I said to myself. That was what it was all about.

We took a zig-zag route when we re-entered Syria.

One night, near Homs, we were so tired we slept on the grass by a river. The ancient giant wheels with their buckets, turned continuously by the water, made squeaking, moany noises. They hypnotized me, made me feel so relaxed I didn't want to move on.

In the morning I lay there, watching the children playing out an ancient ritual, climbing on to the buckets and jumping down, their thin supple bodies brown against the blue sky. They competed with each other in a game that may well have been played for 3000 years. Yes, I could stay here for ever.

"Come on, Toon, don't you want to get to Turkey?"

The worst part of the journey was behind us - riding the scooter no longer took up all our energy. As the roads improved we began to talk. We talked about the black-skinned bedouins in their tents with their breasts exposed and their faces veiled, about the sky so different now from the haze of the desert, about what lay ahead of us.

What changes would there be when we left Asia? Even in Turkey we shared a spiritual identity. We heard the same Muslim call to prayer just as dawn was breaking, *"Allah-ho-Akbar"*, as we had done since we were children in Northern India.

Turkey took a long time to cross, but the roads were good and the hospitality the best we experienced.

Still we often arrived in a new place, unknown and absolutely starving.

"Start smoking, Toon, then you won't feel so hungry."

"But if we've got no money for food, we've got no money for cigarettes."

"You don't need money."

Nitish showed me how to pick up butts from the floor with a dirty hanky and the little ropes which hung down, burning, from which to light up.

"Nobody buys cigarettes in Turkey."

The first two or three days were awful. I hated smoking. Then I got into the habit, felt good and didn't feel hungry any more.

If I could have seen the Jamaican hypnotist swinging his metronome some 30 years later, describing cut-up lungs, overpoweringly smelly and dark with tobacco, in an effort to stop my 60 a day, would I have started picking up the butts?

If I'd known even that wouldn't work beyond a month and I'd take it up again, smoking even more than before, until I stopped of my own accord, past 60, because of the cost, would I have persisted after those awful first days?

At the time, it was a simple way of assuaging hunger until the next piece of luck. And there were plenty of those in Turkey.

By Lake Tuz we came across a man who fed us because he thought we were interesting.

"Look," he said. "I've got a boat. You can stay in my boat by the beach."

It was June.

We were woken from a deep sleep by bitter cold and howling wind. We looked out of the boat. A snowstorm? No, it was pelting down with hailstones. We started running and wrestling with each other to keep warm. We were wet and so were the blankets. We slept for half an hour, got up and ran around, then slept for another half an hour. It didn't worry us - we'd become very hardy.

In the morning, our host took us out in the boat with his wife and a picnic. We jumped into the lake from the boat and explored the water beneath, with snorkels. The lake was clear, like a sky, and full of beautiful coloured stones.

We set off again with full stomachs. Petrol for the scooter cost a shilling a gallon. Wherever we filled up, we were waved aside.

"No, you can't pay for that. You just go with our compliments. *Salaam Walekum.*"

"*Walekum Salaam.*"

Hungry again. But just outside a village near Ankara we met a teacher who spoke quite good English and asked us to give a talk. She taught in a day school for young children, a building of wood and brick, with Turkish carpet on the floors and pieces of carpet on the low benches, smelling of midday meal.

The school provided accommodation in a guest house and we offered to do any work in return, sweep floors, paint walls, or whatever.

"No, we are grateful for your visit. You are real ambassadors of your country and we are learning so much from you. We wish we could make journeys like yours."

In Adapazari we were taken to the top of a beautiful, green hill to see the sunset.

"I'm going to sing and play music for you," said our friend.

The instrument was not more than two feet long and had two strings. The wistful playing and the singing and the sunset wove a special kind of magic.

We were approaching Uskadar, just before Istanbul. A ferry made the trip across the Bosporus every 20 minutes. It was not only the first time we'd left land, but it marked the end of Asia Minor and the beginning of Europe. We were jubilant.

Istanbul, on the other side, was a beautiful city whose buildings breathed history.

"You must have travelled a long way. I watched you go into the shop. I've been waiting for you."

The young scholar who stood by the scooter, Ahmet, was to become a close friend.

"My mother would love you to come and stay as long as you like."

We took off our shoes to enter the small house and were given lovely Turkish slippers to wear. It was like coming home. Their hospitality was second to none, but we couldn't stay for ever.

Gone, with Turkey, went the link with our familiar life. We didn't realize Greece would be so primitive - the roads here were awful - but it was still a strange new culture. The sounds of Muslim prayer were replaced by church bells, the dress was different, and so was the architecture. Even the naan bread, our staple diet so far, suddenly disappeared in Greece to be replaced by European, leavened bread.

I lay by the side of the road, still softened from a wonderful sleep, the sun had come out, our clothing was drying and it was lunchtime. Dark, short-cropped children from a nearby school thronged round the scooter as Nitish started packing up.

A teacher, colourful in the now familiar skirt and headscarf, invited us to give a talk to the school. After our talk a concert was organized and the children sang their hearts out.

They paid us, found us a place to stay in part of the school with the boarders, and fed us for two days.

We still arrived in Yugoslavia with nothing.

CHAPTER 16

Turkey To London

I succeeded in selling my watch - the one I'd tried to sell in the Thieves Market in Calcutta - for 2000 dinars, hardly enough money to buy us food on the way to Belgrade.

Belgrade was awash with flowers. We arrived there at about ten o'clock on a beautiful evening. It had been a hot day, with puncture after puncture. Students were milling around in the university area but there were no cars to spoil the quiet, relaxed atmosphere, only bikes. It was a novelty for us to see the streets lit and all the faces white.

All we had left was a paper note worth less than a penny. I tore it up and threw it into the air. The pieces floated away on the evening breeze like little planes.

"What have you done, you silly fool, throwing away money?" said Nitish.

"You can't buy anything with that."

"You could buy one cigarette."

Our angry voices challenged the peaceful evening until a little crowd of students formed round us. They started examining the scooter. One young man spoke English.

"Where have you come from?"

"Calcutta."

"From Calcutta, all the way?"

"Yes of course all the way. Look on the side of the scooter."

"Where are you going to stay tonight?"

"We've got no money, no nothing. Can you tell us where we can sleep, a park or somewhere?"

I suddenly noticed Nitish, surrounded by five girls who were examining his teeth, comparing the complexion of their hands with his, and laughing. One girl in particular seemed to be drawing his attention. I looked at his face, alarmed.

"Look, Nitish, we're on a world trip. You're not going to fall in love with anyone. We don't want anything to hold up our journey. Prime object travel."

But it was too late. Her name was Lena. She had dark wavy hair and her beautiful brown eyes were wide apart giving her a look of surprised innocence. Her skin was very white.

We sold our story in the morning and became celebrities for a few days. We were invited to stay on the university campus, free.

"Did you know Nehru was coming next week?"

We'd seen the arches made with beautiful coloured decorations and branches of trees, but hadn't realized these were for Nehru's visit to Marshal Tito. A stroke of luck for us as we were taken special care of and even invited by Marshal Tito to his palace right at the top of the hill.

"How do you do?"

"How do you do?" we answered nervously.

The conversation was conducted via an interpreter after that, but didn't improve. So much for all the high dignitaries we met - we had nothing to say to each other.

The food held our interest though - mountains of it spread out for guests to help themselves, and champagne. We made the most of it. Just as well - seven days and 200 miles later we would be really starving again.

But before that, the beautiful Lena had to be left behind.

"Please, Toon, just one more night."

His pleading eyes were hard to resist.

"All right, but we must definitely leave on Sunday, Nitish."

We'd already stayed in Belgrade longer than we'd intended. This would make it nine days.

Sunday. I stared at the scooter, dumbfounded.

"Who could have done that?"

Both tyres were badly punctured. And the tyres were already so fragile.

All sorts of crimes are committed in the name of love. Nitish and Lena achieved one more day in each other's company.

But on Monday they had to part. Heart-rending. Both of them were crying and crying. I turned away.

My last image of Belgrade was Lena demure in her black skirt and jacket, white blouse with the Peter Pan collar and white gloves, standing in the road looking lost and alone.

There were few cars on the main road across Yugoslavia but we couldn't travel at any speed because of the tyres. There were only dry biscuits left to eat. Nitish was very quiet.

We turned off before we met the coast at Rijeka.

We'd become expert at mime by now. The thin man understood that we were very thirsty and had no money. He beckoned us. His face was surprisingly young in spite of the weathered, wrinkled skin. We followed him.

He led us to a sort of bungalow, little more than a hut - he had a smallholding where he raised poultry and goats. In contrast to his worn thinness his wife was plump and young-looking. We sat on foot-high stools round a hand-made wooden table, drinking goat's milk with cheese and home-baked bread. We showed them on the map where we'd been. The man could hardly read or write but his wife was literate.

They wouldn't let us go so we stayed the night, gestures and smiles supplementing the three words of Yugoslav we had in common. In the morning they sent us on our way with a good supply of the goat's cheese and bread wrapped in old newspaper.

We were running out of fuel as well as money. We thought we could get some at Trieste, but couldn't. Would we make it to Venice?

"Nitish, look, we're in luck again. It's all downhill."

As far as we could see the road sloped down. After all, Venice was mostly water. We accelerated and switched off the engine - we'd learnt by now that we could double our distance on the same amount of petrol by taking advantage of any gradient - and coasted for about ten miles. But there was hardly any fuel left.

We ran out 200 yards from the first petrol station just outside Venice. We'd put enough money by for a little fuel but as usual the attendant laughed at us and filled us up for free.

The sky was darkening although it wasn't night as we parked the scooter in one of the piazzas. Venice was fascinating, even when the rain started. The reflections of the tall, narrow houses in the canal through the rain, made the canal look like an actual road, one of the shiny-surfaced roads of our dreams. We nearly walked into it.

"Coffee?"

We still had some bread and cheese left, but the idea of sitting in a café out of the rain for a while was quite attractive.

Inside the café we saw our first television - black and white with a very small screen. A boxing match. The commentary merged with the sound of rain outside and hypnotized us.

Eventually we went back to the piazza.

"Round the world? What are you doing? Where have you come from?"

A handsome young man and his girlfriend were walking all round the scooter, examining it. They'd seen the writing on the side.

"Calcutta? That's amazing. We'd like to go to Calcutta. Come on. Let's go and sit somewhere and drink this."

They said they were Belgian and their names were Robert and Arlette. They had strong liquor and lots of food with them. It had stopped raining. We sat by a canal and dangled our feet in the water while gondolas with their lights drifted by and reflections wavered like mirages in the desert. It was a marvellous, timeless evening.

Nitish and I, unused to strong alcohol, grew very merry. The music flowed from my mouth-organ, sounding to my ears more tuneful than ever before.

"Where are you going to stay?"

The evening was over.

"We don't know. We'll just sleep somewhere and sell our story in the morning."

"No, you come along with us," said Robert, "to our hotel."

The scooter was no match for the couple's powerful motorbike. It was difficult to keep them in sight. We raced over the bridge. A bump and we were airborne, really flying through the night. It was fantastic, unreal. We landed as the back light of the motor bike disappeared into the distance. We'd hit a sandbank.

"Let's have a look at the scooter."

We gave it a couple of kicks and it was fine.

"Are you hurt?"

"Only this little gash in my leg," I said. "We'll have to sleep where we are. We'll get some money from our story in the morning."

But half an hour later, Robert came back for us. "What happened to you?"

We followed him to his hotel.

"Park your scooter somewhere round the back. Arlette and I will sleep on the bed and she will pinch a mattress for you to sleep on the floor."

We climbed through a window - it was two o'clock in the morning.

"We'll see to breakfast. Don't you worry about anything."

"Are you sure you're doing the right thing?"

"Hotel owners have pots of money. You are special people. Don't worry," said Robert.

At elevenish, we walked out of the front door. Our haggard appearance and shabby clothes attracted a few stares but nobody challenged us.

Our story brought us enough money for the next two or three days. Next stop Genoa. We had to ride the scooter very slowly because the wheels were almost square now, repaired and patched so many times. In Italy, the land of scooters - every family had one, mother, father and baby on the seat and the children on the running board - it would have been easy to buy tubes and tyres, but we had no money for that.

We were beginning to get used to Europe. Everyone was marvellously purposeful. They were all busy doing something at the right time, even if they were just sitting. But their affluence didn't make them easy-going - I'd been wrong about that. They were more time-conscious, less relaxed than people back in India.

The shops had ceased to amaze us and we no longer found it strange that there were no animals wandering about in the roads. Everything was ordered.

We arrived in Genoa in slippers - our shoes had completely worn out. Down a lane off the beaten track we found some cheap Italian food. We parked the scooter with my tiger skin gloves on the seat. In the middle of our meal a boy picked up the gloves and walked away. I jumped up.

"Don't take my gloves. They're so important to me."

The boy started running and dropped one glove. I stroked the tiger markings, curved stripes, yellow and brown, and remembered my tiger's eyes. A bad omen? No. I wore a different glove on each hand after that, keeping my one tiger-skin glove like a mascot.

We arrived at the Vespa Headquarters in Genoa at lunchtime the following day, as arranged. A huge crowd had formed in front of the multi-storey building and when the journalists and photographers converged we realized all this was for us. We'd made the best and finest trip ever on a 125cc scooter from Calcutta to Genoa. We'd won the prize - 100 guineas' worth of Italian money.

"But we did have to put the scooter on a truck for two or three hundred kilometres in the desert."

"Forget about that."

So we bought beautiful Italian moccasin shoes - soft and black, very shiny and very comfortable. We bought new shirts, new trousers, we ate well, we stayed in a nice hotel. Our photographs were in the Vespa showcases and in all the Italian newspapers.

"We'll take the scooter," said the Vespa people.

"But what are you going to do to it?"

"We'll recondition the engine and give you brand new wheels."

"For God's sake don't change the frame and dents and all that."

"Of course we won't. We'll keep the exterior exactly as it is."

"Could we have a spare wheel?"

"Oh, yes."

And off went the scooter to the Piaggio Pontedera factory, where the first Vespas were made.

"You'll have to give it a name, you know," somebody said. "Such a famous scooter."

"Why not call it Sabrina?"

So we called the scooter Sabrina and when it came back we painted the name on the front. By now there was hardly any money left and we were ready to leave for Switzerland.

St Gotthard Pass. Snow and no skis. We slid down on our new shoes and marvelled at the views. But the mountains in Kashmir would have dwarfed these mountains, and Switzerland seemed littered with houses and people. How wonderful, how unique, was Kashmir. It was the nearest I got to being homesick.

At the Youth Hostel in Geneva the Chairman of European Vespa invited us to visit.

"We haven't any decent clothes."

"You're all right as you are. You are world travellers. You come to this restaurant." He gave us an address and a time.

We had our new shoes and one reasonable shirt and pair of trousers but we still looked very shabby after travelling round Switzerland. As we got nearer the restaurant, the surroundings became more and more wealthy-looking and impressive. We parked Sabrina outside with rows of other scooters. The restaurant looked so posh we got cold feet.

"Come on, Nitish. I think we'd better go somewhere else. We've got enough money to eat."

But just as we were turning to go, a huge black limousine drew up, a man got out, came between us and put his arms round our shoulders.

"Where are you going, gentlemen? We are so proud of you two. What is worrying you?"

"Our clothes. Because you are all so well-dressed. If we had our national costume - loin cloth, embroidered overshirt ... but we haven't."

"But it's your company we want."

There were 40 people round the beautifully set table, under the chandelier. A seven-course meal had been prepared, avoiding beef in deference to our religion. We ate and ate as only people familiar with starvation can. The wine flowed. I had to give a speech in English - with a French interpreter - about the highlights of the journey. I wonder what I said.

We had tremendous publicity and earnt a lot of money from our story in Switzerland, so we could afford to travel all over the country. But money in Europe didn't seem to last very long. It just seemed to run away. We needed a proper job.

On to Germany. We were getting used to these little countries with their borders and their distinct identities, so unlike the vastness of India.

We arrived at the youth hostel in Stuttgart in July, desperate for a job. We understood that from now on we wouldn't be given food. We'd have to work for it. Fine, if we could get a job.

"Well, what can you do?" they asked us at the youth hostel.

"I could work with my hands - welding or something."

They sent us to Adolf Höschle, a subsidiary of Mercedes-Benz, where the boss's son spoke English and was very helpful.

I cut pieces of iron for the sides of trailers and shaped them in a furnace. The firm made hydraulic rams. It was my first job since selling typewriters in Calcutta and it felt good.

Nitish and I worked there for three weeks, the only brown faces.

Were these Europeans so different from us? Were they stronger? The streets and buildings were more ordered, more sophisticated, church bells rang instead of Muslim calls to prayer, knives and forks clattered instead of quiet fingers, affluence seemed to have made for more tension rather than less. The Germans in particular definitely hadn't got time.

At least we knew where we stood from now on. We'd be given respect for what we'd achieved, but not a free ride. That was all in the past.

CHAPTER 17

Speed was vital if we were to take up the second job the youth hostel had found us - another three weeks with a youth project, helping to build a children's school in Eaubonne, near the Louvre. We had to be in Paris by Sunday evening.

Miles and miles without a stop, so tired, moving so slowly, like a dream ...

What ...?

We'd both dozed and fallen off Sabrina. It was four o'clock in the morning, but August and warm enough to sleep where we lay. The scooter was unharmed as we'd been travelling so slowly. Nothing to worry about.

We were woken three or four hours later. A farmer's children were kicking us to see what was under the blanket beside the battered scooter. Two funny brown men.

Apart from that sleep we rode almost continuously, a 36 hour marathon - and made Paris on time.

At least ten different nationals were involved in the Eaubonne project, staying at the youth camp. In the evenings we sat on the steps of the school building, drinking wine and listening to the soulful notes of Cy's trumpet, just as we'd sat round the neem tree in Patna listening to Sumantro's flute.

Cy the trumpeter and 16-year-old Maureen had just got married at Gretna Green and this was their honeymoon.

"What kind of songs did you hear riding through the desert?" asked the journalist from France Soir.

"Mainly French songs as it was a French-dominated area. There was a loudspeaker by the beach in Beirut." After 5000 miles of burning sun it had been good to sit by the beach and listen to French music.

The journalist seemed delighted with this reply.

"You must have heard Lucienne Delyle then?"

"Who?"

"You admired her, didn't you? You heard her as you rode through the desert and she lifted your spirits. You were so eager to meet her, you sailed right through to Paris."

"Did we?"

"She is coming to Paris now. I can arrange an interview with her. It'll give you a lot of publicity, you'll earn some money. And what a good story it will be."

Ah, now we understood.

All the traffic in the Champs Elysées stopped when Lucienne Delyle arrived that Saturday, and everything was cleared. Thousands of people waited to greet her.

Paris and Lucienne

The journalist was as good as his word. He even organized a reception for us with the famous singer in the Café St Georges.

We put on a splendid act. Lucienne didn't speak English any more than we spoke French so our adoration was passed through an interpreter. It made her feel good to have been such an inspiration to us.

Of course she signed her photograph for the journeybook. She had big dreamy eyes, long dark lashes and a smooth creamy complexion even in black and white. And she filled one of the pages with her French good wishes.

In the evening we went to hear her, for the first time. She was given a fantastic welcome and sang to a packed house. She wasn't bad.

On 31st August the newspapers were full of photographs - Lucienne sitting side-saddle on Sabrina, elegant legs crossed, face upturned to receive kisses from Nitish and me, or the three of us with one arm raised, or Nitish and I alone astride the scooter waving, framed by the distant Arc de Triomphe. There was even a cartoon of Lucienne meeting an Indian in furs. The French seemed amused by my fur-lined jacket and hat and Nitish's ski cap.

The two Hindus on their world tour became famous overnight. "Paris is theirs," concluded one article.

It was a lucky fluke that our "arrival" coincided with that of Lucienne. She was the first person we asked after as we got off our machine, according to one paper. Several articles stated that it was in Calcutta we'd first heard her, by the Ganges not the desert, and indeed that was what had inspired us to make the trip at all. We had to visit Paris to see our idol. We had travelled 16,000 kilometres (or 17,000 depending on which paper) for this very meeting.

Nitish was quoted as saying that his cup was full now that he'd seen the Eiffel Tower and "Madame Thing".

When the three-week contract at Eaubonne was up, and our brief moment of fame was over, we moved to rue St Jacques. We slept on mattresses on the floor in the gymnasium, part of the university, for just a few francs because we were registered as students.

As students we could use the subsidized canteen run by the Sorbonne - the meals were good and we met interesting people. We were also able to pick up enough jobs with the other students, decorating for example, to keep us going.

One of the students, Michel, became a special friend. Not many families here wanted us to mix with them, but Michel's family was a wonderful exception. They were lovely. And where else could I learn about people's lives in other countries, if not in families?

We'd been living in Paris for a couple of months and were due to depart for London in a few days. London itself. One leg of the journey would be complete.

Nitish would stay in London for treatment and I would continue, eventually, on my trip round the world - South Africa, United States, China ...

It was Sunday lunchtime, a beautiful autumn day, and we were going to visit Michel's home for the last time before we left Paris - we'd been invited to have a meal with his mother and sister and cousins in St.Germain-des-Prés.

The Boulevard St Michel was a very wide road, quite steep at the top. Sabrina gathered speed as we sailed down the slope. Autumn leaves in the Luxembourg Gardens on our left glowed against the clear blue sky. In front of us slightly to the right we could see Notre Dame and behind it the brilliant white dome of Sacré Coeur. Life was good. Very soon we'd be sharing a delicious meal with our friends and then in a few days we'd be off on our travels again.

Who would have thought that cars in France could pull out from the right hand side and had right of way even if they were in a small lane turning onto a main street?

Boum!

Nitish screamed and leapt off the scooter. The black Citroen had given us no time at all. We'd collided with the back door.

I picked myself up from the road and started shouting at the driver in Bengali, *"Tumi kee korecho pajichellay?"* The driver, a black student, shouted back in French.

Nitish had landed on the pavement, falling on top of three women and slightly hurting all of them.

As the scooter skidded the left side of my body had made impact with the car. Something was horribly wrong with my knee and blood was pouring from my left hand.

"Ma!" The word tore through my lips.

It was about 1.15 pm on 2nd October, Gandhi's birthday. In Calcutta it was early evening and Ma was blowing into the conch shell as she did every day about that time, blowing the ghosts away with the lovely sound.

"Ma!" she heard, and nearly dropped the shell.

"Toon is in trouble."

Baba agreed that she should write. The letter was posted on 3rd October. "I know you've been hurt..."

How had I got to my mattress in rue St Jacques? The pain had started soon after my cry. It was so awful, so agonizing. I was going to die. They hadn't told me I'd die so young - was it in my horoscope? I lay there, covered myself up, took a couple of aspirin.

"You'll have to sort Sabrina out, Nitish," I mumbled through my haze of pain. The handlebar was pretty badly bent but it hadn't looked as though there was much serious damage.

More aspirin. Aspirin every hour. If only someone would cut off my leg. In and out of consciousness. Morning, alone on the floor. A woman with a broom - no, not Ma - seeing me and screaming out. More people, carted away. Nitish there? And a nurse?

Put in a wheelchair.

"We're taking you to the university hospital."

"I have to go before the end of this week," I said to the big doctor with the white coat. "Have to set off for London. Last bit of the first leg of our world trip."

"Yes, we'll see to that," said the doctor with a lovely smile, and stuck the needle in. Morphine.

When I came to, my left leg was covered with a white sheet, resting at an angle of 45 degrees above the horizontal and my left hand was strapped up at angle of 70 degrees. The feeling of numbness was very pleasant.

"A few hours later and we'd have had to chop off your leg," said the doctor. "A piece of metal had got into your knee and gangrene had started. Thank God for penicillin. Your ankle's chipped and your knee broken but you're all pinned up. You should be all right."

My left knuckle was also broken.

Five days later Ma's frantic letter arrived.

"I'm in fantastic shape," I wrote back. "Feeling so well." I told her about Michel and how kind his family were.

Two weeks after the operation they put my leg in plaster from the toes to the top of the thigh.

"You'll be hobbling for five or six months, but you're in very good shape and you have the right attitude of mind."

I'd fallen in love with all the nurses. Which one could be my wife?

"Come on, give me a kiss - ah lovely."

"We've never known anyone like you with a broken this, that and the other cracking jokes and kissing us," they said.

Michel's mother kissed me too, and brought me fruit. There were lots of visitors. Nitish told me the scooter was repaired free of charge when he showed the journeybook.

Now there was a bigger worry. The hospital bill would be high and the accident was legally my fault. But the money just wasn't there. I knew Baba would pay if I couldn't, in the end. For now though, he and Ma mustn't know about the accident. And I hadn't taken a single rupee from him for this trip.

The time was approaching when the nurses would have to come to my aid. Would they agree? Their faces looked so angelic in the frame of their white headdresses. I was still in love with all of them.

"I can walk now," I told the doctor. "When am I going to be released?"

I needed to know a day or two before so that I could plan my escape. I couldn't wait.

CHAPTER 18

It was in the black silent early hours that the nurses lowered me on to the ground in a sheet out of the first floor window. They giggled nervously as they played out the rope knotted to my sling.

Sh! What if somebody heard us? Discovery was a more alarming possibility than sudden collision with the ground.

There was no sign of Nitish down below. He would be in hiding with Sabrina of course. But what if he wasn't there for some reason? I could hardly go far without him.

Bump. Landing was gentle, the sheet-sling collapsed around me and the nurses blew me good-luck kisses. I hobbled over to a line of bushes, and hidden behind these on the path waited Nitish. Relief. Sabrina stood beside him, propped up on the stand.

There was no sign of the nurses when I turned for one last look. Even the one with the baby face and soft blonde curls had disappeared from the window. The journey had to be finished.

We'd worked it all out. Nitish had a good sense of balance so learning to ride hadn't been difficult. My left leg, the one in plaster, was to be laid straight out on the running board and tied by the left foot.

In practice it wasn't so easy to get the leg in position, especially in a hurry.

"Leave the scooter on its stand until the last minute," advised Nitish, and eventually we roared off into the night.

The first few hours of freedom were spent, not too comfortably, in the warm Gare du Nord. We left for Boulogne early in the morning to catch the noon ferry. Riding pillion felt strange, and the leg was painful.

We crossed the choppy English Channel in a haze of seasickness. When the white cliffs of Dover with red lights twinkling at the top were vaguely outlined against the sky, it was five o'clock, cold and already dark. Reflections of other boats wavered eerily in the water, the horns boomed mournfully and a customs official was bored.

"How did you get the scooter from Syria to Lebanon without the *carnet de passage* being signed?"

Nobody else had spotted this omission. Chilled, tired and empty with sickness, we waited for hours while he worried the problem to death.

"How did you get here? Was it the same scooter? Did you buy another one?"

At last we were freed into the late October night. We knew we wouldn't arrive in London until the early hours after this delay. The sky was overcast with no stars or moon and a cold dampness pervaded the air. A cup of tea might pick us up.

We stopped at the first pub out of Dover, at ten o'clock. A roaring fire welcomed us.

"Do you make tea?"

Laughter all round.

"No. We sell beer."

We weren't used to drinking beer. It did nothing to dispel our tiredness. Progress after that was even slower, prolonged stops every 15 miles to rest and read directions. Directions to London - that thought alone cheered us up. And at least Sabrina seemed to thrive on the cold. She purred. We tried to keep our spirits up.

Could this be London?

Nitish slowed down.

The street was eerily quiet and shabby under the dim gas light. But it had the feel of a big city fringe - shops and buildings seemed to spread for ever into the distance.

Nitish stopped the scooter near a pillar box under one of the gas lights and stretched. I moved my plaster-bound leg painfully off the running board and looked about me, at all the litter on the filthy pavement and the shops with their grimy shutters down.

Could this be London? Where were the polished roads?

The sky was still cold and moonless, it was 2.30 in the morning and we were desperately tired. Not the best time to have a dream shattered.

There was nobody much about except for a policeman, walking up and down the pavement, hands clasped behind his back. He came towards us, pace steady, eyes alert.

"Where are we, Officer?"

"You're in Lewisham. What are you doing here at this time of night?"

"We've just arrived from Calcutta."

"Calcutta? Don't give me that."

He liked our story. Nitish brightened. *"Aykarnay cha pawa jabay?"* he whispered to me. Would he have tea? We knew that only in India and Pakistan and England can they make good tea. It had been a long time since India and Pakistan.

We were in luck.

"I was in Calcutta in the war. Come on, follow me."

Two beautiful cups of tea at the police station, and toast! London wasn't so bad.

"Where are you going to stay?"

"If you could show us the way to Hyde Park we'd be grateful."

"Hyde Park? Why do you want to go to Hyde Park?"

"Well we can sleep on a bench and sell our story to Fleet Street in the morning."

"There are thousands of Indians in London. Haven't you any relatives?"

"No. Only a cousin of my uncle and I don't like him."

"They might let us sleep on the floor." Nitish spoke in Bengali but the policeman understood.

"Nobody's allowed to sleep on the floor of a police station in this country. Now you two lads, how much money have you got?"

"Please wait." I emptied my pockets - I'd changed everything into English money and now I counted it. "One pound nine shillings and eleven pence. That's our lot."

"And you've nothing else?" The policeman looked incredulous.

"No. We got here, didn't we? We thought we'd have no money at all. In a lot of other places we arrived hungry and with nothing."

We were given another piece of toast by a smiling lady in blue uniform. Our policeman was ringing round for a bed.

"Can we have another cup of *cha*?" Nitish asked in Bengali. Two more cups arrived.

"Yes. We've found somewhere for you. You follow me on the scooter."

The police car stopped in a dimly lit street. We unloaded a few things from the scooter and were met by a very sleepy lady with three front teeth missing and lots of wrinkles.

"There you are. Fifteen shillings for both of you."

The bed was huge. We were used to sleeping together. Nitish snored a lot but I would give him a kick to turn him onto his side and get a bit of peace.

"Do you want the money now?"

"No, you get to bed."

We sank into it and knew nothing more until we got up and looked out and it was dark.

"It must be early in the morning."

"No. We came early in the morning."

It was five o'clock in the evening. We'd slept right through.

"I kept looking at you but you were both so peaceful I didn't want to wake you up. Give me 15 minutes."

We inhaled the lovely smell of sausages and eggs frying in used fat and toast singeing at the edges. We were used to eating anything and everything we were given - camel, buffalo, goat, dog. But this was something special, an English breakfast.

"Boys, you're having English breakfast at six o'clock in the evening."

"It's so late now. Can we stay another day?"

"You can stay as long as you like."

I told her how much money we had but assured her we'd earn more when we sold our story.

"I don't know about that but anyway you can stay another day because you came so early in the morning. Up till twelve o'clock tomorrow will do and you can have another free breakfast."

"Madam, you're so kind."

We went to Fleet Street and sold our story for six guineas. We felt so rich.

"How about giving our lady some chocolates or something?" I said.

"A bunch of flowers?" suggested Nitish.

So we gave her both and she let us stay seven days without paying a penny. We wanted to take her out so we asked her what English people did.

"I'm Jewish but it doesn't matter. I'm English too. You can take me for English tea."

The tea house was not too posh, but cleaner than most places then, and the scones and jam were wonderful.

We needed to earn more money while we were still news - people would forget about us soon enough.

The BBC was easy to find at 200 Oxford Street - a huge building with an old-fashioned lift.

"We've just arrived from Calcutta. Who can we see?"

"Talk to the lift wallah, with the big moustache."

"What do you two lads want?"

He told us we needed to see a gentleman called Philip Daly on the fourth floor - London calling Asia.

"So you two lads have come across the Atlantic in a schooner?" said Mr Daly.

"No, no, no. Who told you that story? We travelled on a 125cc scooter and clocked up 11,700 miles." I started talking about bandits ...

"Stop, stop. Have you ever been on a live radio programme before?"

"Yes, in Stuttgart, and spoke German without understanding a single word of it."

"How did you do that?"

"This lovely lady wrote it down and I just read it. We earnt 40 Deutschmark."

"We can't pay you like that but we'll give each of you one guinea a minute."

"That'll do," I said. "Very kind of you."

Mr Daly impressed on us that this would be a live programme, called the Commonwealth Overseas Programme, transmitted all over the world, short wave. It would start at twelve (5.30 pm in Calcutta) and it was now only ten to twelve, so there was time.

We were led to a dark room with table, notebook and huge microphone. We sat opposite a Mr Edwards who said "Listeners, ladies and gentlemen, good afternoon. We have two very interesting lads sitting here just come across the Sahara Desert - "

"No, not Sahara. Iranian Desert."

" - clocking up 11,700 miles on a scooter, and it's a pleasure to introduce you to Toon Ghose and Nitish Biswas. You were telling us earlier that you got caught out by bandits. Can we hear about that?"

They could, and much more.

Nitish was hitting me hard on the knee. "I can speak also in English and you're talking all the time. What about me? I was on the pillion."

"Not in that part of the desert. And you can't speak English."

"I beg your pardon!"

"Not the way I do. I've been to an English public school."

"You're not giving me a chance."

Our argument on the air didn't seem to detract from the interest in us. Because it was lunchtime about 500 people were listening in the BBC building. As we came downstairs we were applauded from every side. The interview was a tremendous success, we had lots of enquiries from it and became very well known - briefly as usual. We were heard on the radio programme "In Town Tonight," had articles in motor cycle magazines, newspapers ...

The following week we pre-recorded instalments of the story for the BBC Commonwealth Programme, two or three minutes of chat and four minutes of story at a time. The last instalment, the Paris accident, was broadcast months later, in January. Baba translated it for Ma in Calcutta. There, what had she said? Ma wrote immediately.

"Toon, you have lied to me about this. I knew you were in trouble because I heard you distinctly. We'll talk about this when we meet again."

Mr Daly invited us to appear on television in the programme "Asian Club." He wrote, impressing on me the need for punctuality "due to the presence of Princess Margaret during the rehearsal". A coach took us from Oxford Street into the exalted atmosphere of Lime Street, while I went over the text of the speech which had been written for me and which I was supposed to memorize:

"...We thank you very much Sir John that you have such wonderful policemen in your force ..."

There were other wonderful people around London that grey November. Nitish and I were strap-hanging in the tube to Earls Court where we then lived, talking in Bengali about a fellow passenger.

"*Kee shundor meye!* What a beautiful girl!"

"My God, what a gorgeous rosy complexion, such blonde hair."

"Don't you go falling in love again, Nitish."

The young woman fascinated us. We continued to sing her praises.

"*Ahmi jani tomrah Kolkuttar chellay.* I know, you come from Calcutta."

Another Bengali voice! We looked eagerly about us. No other Indians, only whites and a Jamaican.

"I'm round here."

A white-haired English gentleman seated round the corner from us smiled broadly.

"Do you live in London?"

"We've just arrived. Our scooter's being repaired by Vespa agents in Bristol ..."

"Over land? That's interesting. I'll give you my card. Please come and visit us. Give me a ring."

We went later to his Knightsbridge flat. He'd been a judge in Calcutta for 30 years and his wife also spoke Bengali, though less well. An array of silver cutlery waited on the polished mahogany table. Fish for starters. Main course potatoes, vegetables and a nice chunk of meat. We both took a bite.

"What meat is this?" asked Nitish.

"Beef."

"What is the meaning of beef?"

"Cow's meat ... Oh, you're Hindus, I hadn't realized." Our hostess was mortified to have made such a mistake.

I felt sick, then I saw Nitish clutch his stomach.

"Can I use your toilet, please?"

Impossible to imagine that a few years later I'd not only have kept it down but eaten it with relish.

Nitish didn't stay long in Earls Court with me. He moved in with some Indian friends while he was receiving treatment for his back.

My leg and hand were still in plaster and the pain had not disappeared. London, in the land of our dreams, was dirty and dreary after the immaculately clean cities we'd been through - Belgrade, Bonn, Stuttgart, Geneva. In parts it was worse than Calcutta.

How I wished I could rise above this dreariness, up through the clouds to where there would be sunshine, quietness and pure air. Then I would be ready to battle with any storms and fight my way through any blinding fog.

But for now flying was still a dream. Planes drifted like silver birds across my mind, and all I could do was hold on, keep going somehow, until my body healed.

CHAPTER 19

As the winter of 1955 progressed, the smog became more frequent. Smog hadn't featured in my dreams of London.

The only job I could find was in an Indian restaurant in West Cromwell Road. I shared a tiny room, no bigger than a coal bunker, with two other kitchen porters. One day, just before Christmas, the smog was so bad I couldn't find my way to this little hole. Even my own hands had disappeared. I blundered along, dragging my leg, all alone in dirty thick cloud.

My leg still gave me pain. The signatures on the plaster were no longer readable. Even the kisses of the baby-faced nurse had been smudged in the mucky dampness of London.

Work in the restaurant was becoming unbearable. And what was the use of London's art galleries, cinemas, theatres and concert halls with my leg to restrict me and no money?

I wandered aimlessly. Once I found myself at Speakers' Corner in Hyde Park where a grey-bearded man with powerful brown eyes stood on a soap box. He was dressed in a black coat and cloth cap, bow tie askew, waving his stick in the air as he slated Anthony Eden.

I looked round anxiously. If anyone had spoken against Nehru like this in Calcutta he'd have been carted away. There were two policemen standing by.

"There's going to be a riot," I said to myself.

Cloth cap became more and more eloquent in his attack on the Prime Minister. Loud cheering from one side and jeering from the other.

"I'd better leave."

I started limping away, out of trouble, but as I looked back another speaker had taken the stage, a tubby unshaven man with bloodshot grey eyes beneath a grey woolly hat. "I'm a communist ..." he said in a strong foreign accent, and the policemen just stood there watching as before. I shook my head in disbelief and left.

One of the policemen reminded me of our Lewisham policeman and the cups of tea and our high hopes and then I became despondent again.

No kites circled high in the skies above Hyde Park, just gangs of pigeons flying low. How long was it since I'd seen the kites we took so much for granted all over India?

I wasn't in a fit state to move on, even if I could shake off my lethargy, but this was no place to hang about. I hadn't travelled so far for this. Something had to happen.

A message arrived.

I'd told the Douglas plant in Kingswood near Bristol, where Vespas were produced in the UK, that I was a scooter instructor and was looking for a job. I felt my claim justified - if I couldn't instruct after such a journey, who could? - but I didn't hold out much hope.

Then one afternoon a message arrived from the Douglas plant. "Got a job for you, teaching an Australian lady who wants to return to Australia via India. There are two of them, wanting to go on two Vespa scooters, but this younger one hasn't even got a sense of balance on a bicycle - we've given up. Can you do something? We can't help you financially but the ladies are very interested and would pay."

I drew a deep breath, rang the number I'd been given and waited nervously. A pleasantly deep feminine voice, Australian accent.

"Yea, we'd love to see you. Where shall we meet?"

We decided on the entrance to Hyde Park tube station.

"You can't mistake me. A grey jacket - slightly torn, a blue shirt, a grey sweater oversize ... But start looking at my left foot - I've just had a leg plaster removed and my swollen toe is sticking out through a hole in my canvas shoe. I've got a moustache and very short hair pointing towards the sky ..."

My hair had just started growing again after a shave to rid myself of lice. In public I blamed my baldness on the more romantic infestation of desert sand-flies.

"... And I'm pretty suntanned."

She started giggling.

"When shall we meet?" I said.

"It would be better for us in the evening, after work."

We fixed on six o'clock.

Slightly before six, by the entrance of Hyde Park tube I spotted a pair of ladies.

"Hello, how do you do? We're supposed to meet here."

Oh my God, no-one had ever looked at me like that. If only the ground would open up and swallow me. I just stood there after that, head down and arms folded.

Ten minutes later I risked raising my head a bit and noticed two ladies with lovely hats, beautifully dressed, gazing down at my toes then up at my face. We looked at each other and the girls burst out laughing. "Toon!"

"Phil and Fay!"

I must have looked like an untouchable beside them. But before I knew what was happening they'd marched either side of me, each putting a hand under my arm.

"Right, we're going to have a cup of tea. English tea."

"No, it's Indian tea."

The three of us entered a very posh restaurant and all of a sudden London seemed a brighter place.

I sat behind Fay on the scooter right from the first "lesson". No sense of balance? We'd see about that. Chalk Farm, Primrose Hill, Hampstead Heath. We flew along. Sometimes I talked about flying.

I'd given up the job in West Cromwell Road and so I had nowhere to sleep, not even a bunker, and the nights were getting colder. "Why not stay with us?" said the girls. Of course it was out of the question.

I walked everywhere. Occasionally I'd come across a road-workers' fire and they'd move aside to let me warm up, their faces friendly in the orange glow. Not many people locked their car doors so sometimes a comfortable Jaguar or a Ford provided a sheltered bed for the night.

I became an expert at protecting myself from the cold with newspapers fished from rubbish bins, but the temperature dropped dramatically on those January nights. One morning I stood outside the house where Phil and Fay lived with 12 other girls and gazed up longingly. But I knew I wouldn't be able to knock on their door when they came back from work.

There was a church nearby with beautiful flowers inside, big daisies - yellow and white - red carnations and fresh green feathery leaves. Winter sun shone through the stained glass windows, dropping pale blobs of blue and orange light on the stone floor. Peaceful. I could sleep on one of the benches undisturbed.

But at night the door creaked eerily as I opened it and a musty smell assaulted me. The darkness inside was threatening and it felt freezing, colder than outside. I closed the door quickly.

In front of the door, before the flight of worn-out grey stone steps, was a level area, six or seven feet deep. Here I made my newspaper bed, swaddled my bare body in newspaper under my clothes and wrapped my feet in newspaper under my socks. My head was encased in the balaclava helmet bought in Delhi, leather outside, yaks' wool inside. I lay down and watched the ghostly shadows from the faint gas lights.

"Have you seen your face, Toon?" said Fay one morning.

Difficult to keep up appearances when you're sleeping rough, even with public baths at Camden Town.

The girls smartened me up and dragged me bodily before their landlady. She looked hard at my face and seemed satisfied.

"You're welcome to live in the same room with Phil and Fay. Good luck to you."

The girls slept head to head, with me on the floor in an old sleeping bag of Phil's. Privacy was a problem which had to be addressed. If any of us wanted to change, we'd shout, "Turn around" and the other two would turn. When anyone went to the bathroom, one of us had to stand outside the door as it couldn't be locked.

The deal was this - I didn't pay for food or rent and they didn't pay for my tuition. I soon got Fay going. Within two months she took the test and passed and also did some advanced training. Teaching was satisfying.

"You must meet this mad Indian who's helping us prepare for our trip to Australia," Phil told Daphne in the office where they both worked.

"Come to dinner."

Daphne was tall and slim with a porcelain complexion and lovely blue-grey eyes. She paid rapt attention to everything I told her about India and was very taken with the story of my travels. She smiled often and I'd never seen such perfect white teeth. I took her out a few times after the party.

It was my turn to be fascinated, by her travels all round Europe and in Bermuda and how much she seemed to know. Her delicate appearance belied her energy and enthusiasm.

It was a casual friendship but she seemed to understand me and her interest in India was genuine. So we kept a correspondence going after I left London, but then lost touch. I'd given her the family telephone number in Calcutta, although I wouldn't be going back myself. She might find it useful if she was sent out there one day ...

I knew from the first I'd be happy in Chalk Farm with Phil and Fay. In the early hours in the middle of January I was having one of my happy dreams. I flew over Hampstead Heath, not in a plane but with my arms outstretched as I had as a child in Lucknow. This time I really took off and there was no-one to stop me.

I flew to a beautiful place I didn't recognize, banked smoothly with one arm down and then flew back again, arms level, nose headed for the mosque-like dome of St. Paul's in the distance, up over the hill, then down again. I gently crashed by the side of Hampstead Ponds and woke up needing to go to the bathroom.

It was all nice and cosy in the sleeping bag - too cosy to move. The room seemed lighter than it should have been and my eyes were drawn towards the big window which reached the floor by my side. Was there somebody in the room above throwing down tiny bits of paper? It seemed so light outside and these bits of paper were floating down. I sat up. The grass and road were getting covered. Oh no, snow!

Still wearing Phil's pyjamas I opened the door quietly and went out. I walked 20 feet down the path and opened the gate. There'd been snow on the mountains in Kashmir but this was the first time I'd seen snow actually falling and it was pure magic. I jumped about in the whiteness like a small boy, stamping my feet, waving my arms and throwing back my head. It was fantastic.

An Alsatian started howling. Coming for me? I ran back, panicking, and shut the gate. Then I realized I must have woken everybody up - all 14 ladies seemed to be leaning out of their windows, watching me.

"Come in you stupid boy," called Phil. "What are you doing?"

Phil and Fay

CHAPTER 20

April 13th 1956 was just how I'd always imagined an English spring day. "Friday 13th?" everybody said, aghast, and I remembered how carefully my own departure date had been planned.

But Fay and Phil, untouched by planetary influences and English superstitions, sat astride their scooters in the Chalk Farm sunshine and beamed, rosy and excited, at the press photographers. Then they were off.

If they'd left on a Thursday it would have been a matter for concern - nobody should start a journey on a Thursday morning, I'd known that since childhood. But Friday was fine. I watched and waved until I couldn't see what I was waving at. What a fantastic journey they were going to have, good times and tough times ...

What was I doing here?

Their landlady was kind letting me stay in the flat for a while, but soon I would have to move on. It wouldn't be the same without the girls anyway. And how was I going to earn enough here to keep myself, let alone have money over to learn to fly? London didn't seem the right place for that in any case, and part of me was relieved.

So what was I doing here?

Fay and Phil were well on their way now. In spirit, I rode with them to Dover, flew across the Channel to Calais, headed back home to India, prepared to cross the sea to Darwin and ride triumphant into Melbourne. Would I ever see Australia? I thumbed through the flimsy pages of my own thick journeybook, bitterly regretting the loss of my diary. Cy Smith, the trumpeter from Eaubonne days, had surfaced in London and begged to borrow it.

"Of course, old chap. You're welcome."

Handing it over, I never imagined Cy would disappear off the face of the earth along with my masterly descriptions of places, my profound observations of life and meticulous records of Sabrina's performance.

No point in dwelling on that. At least there was the journeybook with all the messages, drawings and photos of friends we'd made along the way. Finishing in London.

As far as my family knew, the journey to London was only the first leg. The plan was to continue round the world - on my own this time - via Cape Town, New York, Alaska, Panama, Santiago, China by boat, then overland again to India, safely home. Of course I had no intention of returning to India, but even the names Cape Town, New York, Alaska ... sounded magic to my ears. Especially Cape Town.

"Son, why can't you go to other places? Why do you have to go to Cape Town? We have no diplomatic relations with them at all. It's not right for Indians to go to South Africa."

Mrs Pandit, High Commissioner of the Indian Embassy - and Nehru's sister - had quashed that dream. Had no progress been made since Gandhi's troubled time as a young lawyer in South Africa?

I paused at Stuttgart in my journeybook. Good money to be earned in the factory there and a chance to travel too. A settled period would give me time to think. I reckoned I had just enough money to get to Stuttgart. Why not go?

The decision felt right but somehow I wasn't satisfied with myself. I rode Sabrina aimlessly round London - we were alone now, man and machine.

We stopped at traffic lights and suddenly my body stiffened. Reflected in the back window of the Wolseley in front, a silver plane moved across the spring sky. I twisted my head to catch sight of the original with the fuzzy vapour trail it left behind. Then the traffic moved on. The lights were green.

And light dawned. It wasn't the money or the place making me play for time, stopping me from trying to achieve my aim. It was Baba's angry eyes and the writing I'd never even seen on a yellowing roll of paper - my horoscope. I was gut scared. And something would have to be done about it.

Instead of taking the boat, Sabrina and I would fly across the Channel.

On 6th May 1956 we headed for Ashford Airfield from where we were to travel in a Bristol Freighter to Ostend. My stomach churned with excitement and fear.

I'd allowed plenty of time, but then I hadn't expected hailstones in May. What a crazy country. In India you knew what to expect, heat in the summer, rain in the monsoon ...

The hailstones bounced off the scooter, big as little marbles, perfectly white. In no time at all everything was blocked out by the settling stones and the road too icy to use. That was the first delay.

The hail stopped as abruptly as it started and the ice melted. We were on our way again, images riding through my mind.

"Plane brought down by second unexpected hailstorm ..."

Was this to be the accident Baba had warned against? I could hear Ma wailing. "*Chellay, ahmar chellay*. My son, my son."

But there was no going back now and the quiet airfield of Ashford lay under an innocent sky. Only one aeroplane stood ready to depart - ours.

The second delay was a pretty young lady with blonde hair and blue eyes, a journalist who'd arranged to meet me at the airfield. I posed for her on Sabrina and then the scooter was whisked away to be packed on board. This was it. My heart was thumping.

But the journalist hadn't finished with me.

"What are your plans? Where are you going now?"

"Oh, to North Africa, through Germany, first." That was as good an answer as any.

Questions, questions. Then, "I wish I could come along with you."

So do I, I thought.

Over the Tannoy - "Would the passenger with the scooter please board the plane immediately. The flight is being held back."

Somehow I boarded the plane, my legs jellied with excitement and fear. I was defying Baba and - well, and what? A piece of nonsense or the will of Lord Shiva? I didn't know. The trip was very noisy - deafening in fact - and as comfortable as sitting in a cattle truck. Not easy to think. There weren't many passengers - the plane was mainly for freight. The flight lasted half an hour and the noise didn't stop, jangling my nerves.

It wasn't the sort of flying I really wanted to do but out of the window there was endless sky. At least I was in the air. I'd done it. The ice was broken.

And what relief when we touched down at Ostend. All in one piece.

It was good to get on Sabrina and start riding again. I rode and rode. Puffy cumulus clouds followed us all the way, free as my spirit. I rode through Belgium, Luxembourg and South Germany to Stuttgart, stopping the night in a youth hostel - where? - as if in a dream.

Back to earth. Back at work in the same subsidiary of Mercedes-Benz, from 7 am to 4 pm, half an hour for lunch. First two weeks in a bought tent, then lodging with a fellow worker. Not all work - playing table-tennis in the evenings and through a fellow Indian joining the Indo-German Association.

It was at one of the Indo-German Association meetings in the famous Liederhalle that I met Lotte and her brother Jurgen. Jurgen worked with disturbed children, wanted to devote his life to helping others, to atone in some small way for the atrocities of the war. He also saw it as his personal salvation. Could it be mine? Wasn't it a finer aim than flying?

My meeting with these two had an even greater impact on someone else's life. Having helped Nitish to join me in Germany, I introduced him to Lotte, who was to become his wife.

My travel-hunger still needed feeding with little trips on Sabrina. On a seven day holiday I even reached Casablanca, but had to be transported back, laid low with a terrible bug.

In the factory they taught me a new skill - welding. The work focused my mind until it was time to finish, to relax with a shower and a beer before going home. One day at the bar something caught my interest - a small round badge depicting three seagulls. It was worn by one of the engineers, a bald man with a young face, and I knew the badge had something to do with flying.

"Who is that man? I'd like to meet him."

We were introduced. The badge was called a Silver C, gained by achievements in gliding. Gliding? Flying without a motor, silently, like a bird?

"Come and have a trial lesson with Harmann, why don't you? I only fly for the fun of it."

Should I? Dare I? Glide like a bird?

He must surely have heard my heart hammering away.

CHAPTER 21

Hornberg Gliding Centre was situated on a ridge, 30 minutes' ride from Stuttgart. Harmann was a large fine-looking man in his forties, also sporting a Silver C badge. He spoke good English with a slight American accent, although in my excitement it was difficult to take much in.

"Just enjoy the flight first time round," he said. "I'll tell you what I'm doing."

I stepped into the glider and let him strap me in the front cockpit, my legs stretched out in front of me. Harmann sat behind, the transparent canopy snapped shut over us and there was silence. It was so quiet the rapid thumping of my heart seemed to echo round the cockpit.

"Don't touch this yellow knob. It's the release mechanism."

We were to be launched by winch. I tried hard to concentrate on what he was saying, not on what the hell I was doing here against Baba's wishes.

"... all the checks - canopy, brakes, spoilers locked, straps tight ..."

His voice at least was easy to hear, even through my terror, a surprise after my experience in the Tiger Moth.

"Instruments - altimeter reading zero ... One finger up - take up slack ..."

The ground signaller, seeing one finger, alerted the winch driver half a mile away by waving his yellow flag across his knees, and the cable attaching us to the winch slowly snaked its way into a straight line. The suspense was unbearable.

"Two fingers up - *Auf geht's*, all out."

The signaller waved the flag above his head and we were off.

"Cable taut. Keep the wings level with the movement of the stick to the left and right, keep it straight, keep the direction of the nose with the rudder at your feet. When we've got enough speed, I'll ease the stick back ..."

The noise of the wind increased. Incredible, fearful excitement. The nose pitched up at a terrible angle, 45 degrees at least. My heart nearly stopped.

I couldn't see anything in front of me as we shot upwards, only hear the whistling of the wind and feel the mind-blowing exhilaration.

Suddenly it felt as though my whole body was about to rise off the seat. First experience of negative G. This astronaut sensation sent me out of this world for a flash of a second. Nearly one with God. A feeling I'd never had in the Tiger Moth.

We'd got to the top of the launch - 1000 feet above the ridge, Hermann had moved the stick firmly forward, we'd levelled out and released the cable.

As the nose dropped below the horizon, a wonderful world appeared in front of me - sky, mountains, the river Rhine snaking ... The beautiful valley was 3000 feet below us and we seemed motionless above it.

The whistling of the wind had diminished to a swishing sound as a gentle breeze ran over the canopy.

"Right, I've trimmed the glider level with the elevators which are controlled by the backward and forward movement of the stick. Nose down, nose up - pitching. Stick to left and right - rolling. Rudder to left and right - yawing. It's very important that we have only one landing in a glider. You must remember that."

"Look to your left, we're losing height gently, so we have to remain very near our landing area and keep our eyes on that, not forgetting to keep a very good look out all the time, to right and left, ahead, below, above, for other aircraft."

"Now I'm going to put the spoilers out and land it."

The landing was exhilarating too. We descended steeply, levelled out, made a beautiful touch-down and stopped within a few yards.

"*Sehr schön, nicht wahr*? Beautiful, eh?"

My face must have told him everything. I was hooked.

After three lessons Harmann disappeared and Herbert took over. Herbert was very young and outgoing. Sometimes I understood what he meant and other times I didn't. "Just get on with it, Herr Ghosay," he would say.

I fell in love all over again with flying and with the sky and the silence of the gods. I learnt what to do if in trouble - how to get rid of the canopy and jump out (we always wore parachutes), not to jump if below 2000 feet and to get the glider down - but these were mere words, there were no thoughts of danger now at all.

One day without any warning Herbert strapped me in a single-seater glider called a Grunau Baby. "This glider flies slightly slower, safer. Off you go."

My first solo flight. One finger. Two fingers. No time to think.

Only visual communication with the winch driver was possible. Once the glider was airborne, rolling it by moving the stick from left to right told him that more speed was required whereas yawing the plane from side to side by means of the rudder requested less speed. These signals were quite obvious and enabled the winch driver to adjust the power to give a smooth launch.

So I'd done my waving and I'd got airborne like a donkey's hop, with no time to think about it.

The Grunau Baby had an open cockpit and my training was in a closed one so the noises were unfamiliar - the wind on my face and the strange zzz transmitted through the wire of the winch into the cockpit.

The noises started to increase at a hell of a rate. I raised the nose to get the maximum height possible. Panic set in. I must slow the thing down. Roll from side to side. Was that right? The noise increased incredibly. No, it wasn't.

The wire reached such an angle with the winch that it activated the safety device to free the glider. Pfutt. Thank God - otherwise the glider would have been pulled down and crushed.

Thoroughly shaken and set free. On my own. But I didn't know what I was doing. I shot up like a rocket, then everything went quiet and the glider stalled. Recover - that was quite easy. Relax. Enjoy the silence of the flight, the breeze rushing by, the beautiful blue August sky, the mushroom clouds, the wonderful freedom. I looked down.

"Oh my God, I don't know how to get down."

I was reaching the edge of the upwind side of the ridge from where the gliders were launched and could see down, down on the other side where the ground dropped another thousand feet and everything looked so small. Suppose I couldn't land back on the ridge?

The edge. But I went up, not down and kept going up and up. What was happening? I started screaming. "Oh my God. I'm going to die."

This was it, my destiny, the price of disobedience. All memories of the birds I'd watched soaring in the hills and Herbert's diagrams of arrows flowing up the side and his imperfectly understood warnings - all gone.

"Lord Shiva, *Gott im Himmel*, all gods everywhere, please help me please. If only you can get me down I'll never fly again. I want to come down, please God."

I ranted on in Bengali, German, English and anything else that came into my head. Loud enough for everyone on the ridge that afternoon to hear.

Still going up and up. Then I started thinking and got the spoilers out to lose height, but the lift was so great we were still going up. That was all I could do - put the spoilers out and dive the glider towards the airfield, and pray. I came out on the opposite side, the downward side of the ridge, started losing height at last and managed to land on the long dirt strip. Still alive.

"*Hals- und Beinbruch!*" Half a dozen young men bent me over and slapped me hard on the bottom, wishing me good luck after my first solo. I nearly fainted.

"Ah, Ghosay. *Wunderbar*. But why did you go on the upwards side of the ridge? - I told you about it."

It was unknown for anyone to stay up for so long the first time. The story of my voluble panic spread all over the village. "Poor chap. He'll never fly again."

And I promised myself that I never would, any form of flying. I was frightened to death and had learnt my lesson. I'd come and help launch the gliders, but flying - never.

I'd earned 320 marks that week, a lot of money in those days. I blew the whole lot in the bar.

Life began to weigh on me like a heavy sky. With my dream of flying blown apart, I seemed to lose all sense of direction, groping in the grey. There was someone who could have led me out. But that was turning sour too ... Perhaps I should make myself fly after all, I thought. So what if something happened. It wouldn't matter.

Idle talk. I knew I'd be too scared.

The first accident was my fault. My welding mask was off - only for a second - because it was so unbearably hot. Pain shot through my left eye.

The chip of hot iron had to be extracted and then the pain grew more intense. My vision in that eye was practically gone.

Perhaps that was partly why the hammer missed. Some days later I had the second accident, while shaping hot iron. The hammer missed the iron.

There was no pain for at least a minute, but as if in a dream I saw the smashed knuckles and the strange grey - almost white - and blue of my once brown hand.

Then it started, unbelievable pain. I lay on the hospital bed in agony as my arm swelled to a balloon. I lay there, drenched in pain, as they tried again and again to get the bones back together in the right places.

God, I certainly couldn't fly now. You made sure of that. Work would be out of the question too.

I spent my days sitting on a park bench like an old man, watching the pigeons scrabble in the dust. People hurried by full of purpose, or ambled with happy faces.

Three-quarters of my pay, without overtime, didn't amount to much. The bench made a change from the coal bunker which had become my home. Usually I was left alone in my misery but one day somebody joined me on my bench. He had a very red, puffed-up face and a worn out overcoat. He was obviously sloshed.

"What have you done to your hand?"

"My knuckles are broken so badly I can't go back to work."

A sudden movement sent the pigeons flying, half-heartedly, a few yards down the path.

"Look at the birds flying around," slurred my companion. "Would you like to fly like that?"

"I used to fly, but I'm too frightened now."

"Only birds are supposed to fly, not humans. Flying is a curse to humanity. Planes drop bombs, kill people, kill animals ..." He was warming up, then he suddenly stopped.

"Here have some of this." He handed me the bottle of colourless liquor, said it was called Kirschwasser.

We shared it between us and felt good. This man is talking some sense, I thought. Flying is not for us.

The man passed me again several times but he didn't recognize me. The warm glow had left me quickly too and I sank back into despair, became very low and ill. Asthma had returned with a vengeance, then TB was diagnosed. It was almost a relief to find myself back in a hospital bed for a week. And then Hans came to the rescue.

Hans, an apprentice in the factory, had wondered what had happened to me. He and his journalist father realized I was the same Indian who'd made the newspapers on a world trip the previous year and then Hans heard through one of my friends about the accident and the TB. Knowing how interested his father was in Indians and Hinduism, he took me to his family home - and there I stayed. Gradually life became worth living again, reading, walking, meeting new friends.

One family I met through "my" family, great believers in Gandhi, lived in the countryside - it was a favourite walk of mine to visit them. Sometimes we all walked together in the pine forest nearby, small among the tall trees and wonderful fragrance.

"Don't go off on your own - you'll get lost."

But I began to lose the drift of what they were saying, the forest held me in a trance, I walked on dream-like and everyone disappeared. The tall trees parted to reveal a clearing. I held my breath.

A flock of graceful white herons - egrets - wheeled above me. Magic. And there was hope.

Shortly after this a Mercedes arrived at Hans' house and a gentleman from the Rotary Club, who didn't look as though he was used to being thwarted, took me back to his sumptuous office. He seemed to know everything that had been happening to me and wanted to help. He said my father "requested" me to return home to rest before I resumed my travels. I may have been a long way from Calcutta but I hadn't reckoned with the fraternity of the Rotary Club. It left me with no choice. I was too weak to argue anyway.

I left Stuttgart on 30th November 1957, rode Sabrina to Genoa and boarded the Italian boat, the Lloyd Triestino, for Bombay. For two days storms raged and sea-sickness occupied my time.

I went ashore in Naples and fell flat on my face - it was snowing. From Naples on, the good food and exercise on the boat began to take effect. I'd almost recovered as we squeezed through the Suez Canal into the Red Sea and by the time the boat docked in Bombay there'd been a transformation in my health.

The train journey from Bombay to Calcutta, first class, took 36 hours. A German professor of Indology who was to share my compartment greeted me in Sanskrit.

"What, you don't know Sanskrit? Such a beautiful language."

I thought of the trouble I'd had with the Bengali alphabet and shook my head.

Lulled by my companion's snores, I stared out at the Indian night where few tigers roamed now. I'd ridden across India two years before with such hopes, the first leg to freedom. What was I doing returning to my family, on a train?

CHAPTER 22

Calcutta's Rabindra Lake at dusk was a soothing place. The trees on the far bank were silhouetted soft black against a pink sky. Crows chatted noisily in the branches, then large groups of them detached themselves for a mad dash across the lake. They flew towards a small mosque glowing faintly pink on an island all to itself.

A willowy black-haired girl washed herself at the water's edge, the bright colours of her sari already dimmed in the fading light.

High up a few kites still circled peacefully. Down below bats darted out in lightning circles and, barely visible, a butterfly brushed past. In no time it would be dark, still warm but gently dark.

Not like the slow frosty sunsets of a German winter.

The lake was a place to think and dream, a refuge from the bustle of Calcutta, a refuge from a caring home. Everything had been the same, yet not the same - family, friends. It wasn't they who had changed. Ma blowing every night on the conch shell to keep away the evil spirits, Sheila still in love with her Christian, Dada doing very well in his work - as was to be expected - Baba, exasperated, trying to get his younger son to settle down.

India hadn't changed either. But it wasn't my only point of reference now. It was as if I'd flown high above my country and could put it in perspective, one culture amongst many. The barriers which had seemed so insurmountable from down below, the authority of parents, the threat of an arranged marriage, shrank into insignificance. I was a free person, with no need for guilt. My religion wasn't the only answer to the world and now that I could question the truth, its hold on me diminished, and perhaps its real value increased. But with the polished almirah that housed my horoscope gleaming in the background it wasn't so easy to dismiss astrology.

Blowing the conch shell

Baba saw none of this change, only his younger son returning
to the fold as impossible as ever. I hadn't been round the world,
had to be rescued after two years - and of course there was no
book and no job. What was I going to do, he asked. An office
job? Never.

I'd fallen back into table-tennis coaching, travelling all over
India for exhibitions, but not earning much - and aiming where?
A whole year gone.

Sometimes the scooter trip - the deserts and the cities,
London, Stuttgart - seemed like a dream.

Ma had given me a real good hug when she'd first seen me.

"You lied to me, Toon, about the accident. I love you so
much that whatever happens I'll know about it."

"Yes I did tell a lie because I didn't want to worry you. It
wasn't really a dangerous journey at all."

"Not dangerous? It was all on the radio - you got attacked
by bandits, you went hungry, you landed up in hospital, and
you never asked us for help."

"Well, I got to London."

There were still some things to make the trip seem real - letters and odd telephone calls from friends. They were like little threads waiting for me to grasp and pull myself along. But to where?

The child with one hand who begged at the park gate reminded me of Jurgen and his work in Germany. Was that the way?

Here at the lake, where there was time to think, my two worlds met. The white egrets that had wheeled above the clearing in Germany would stand on the leaves of water plants in the morning sun as if they walked on water. The kites soared like gliders, round and round, higher and higher. Never fly again? Of course that wasn't true. Badly scared but still entranced, my dreams turned to the sky again and again. One day ...

The evening meal would be ready now, the food I'd grown up with, the people I'd grown up with. Ma met me at the door.

"*Tara tari*, Toon, quick. There's a phone call for you."

"I'm in Calcutta! In the Diplomatic Service. I've got a lovely job, two servants, a car ..."

"That's wonderful," I said. Who was she?

"A bit different from the bed-sitter in Swiss Cottage."

"Absolutely." Swiss Cottage? A friend of Phil and Fay?

"We must meet up."

"Yes, we must." Who was she?

Then I found some lovely blue-grey eyes to match the voice. Of course, Daphne. "Yes, we must."

Daphne had plenty of time for platonic friendships since she had an understanding with a doctor back in England. I was pulled into a circle of stimulating people. Dull routine was shattered. Calcutta started to buzz.

I felt oddly relieved when Daphne broke with her doctor, but still the easy friendship suited me fine - until Kutu's birthday in February.

"Aren't you going to this birthday party, Toon?" Daphne had met Kutu, the friend who'd fallen in the lake in Kashmir.

"No, I don't think so," I mumbled.

Why hadn't I realized until now how much I loved her, or why she had broken off with her doctor. I was taken aback.

We never got to the party.

"Come and meet these people," urged Daphne a few weeks later. "They're here to make a documentary. You'll find them interesting."

We sat round Daphne's richly polished table - Philip Donnellan the director, Ken the photographer, Fred his assistant, Daphne and her friends.

Philip was frustrated. He'd advertised for an Indian research assistant, someone who'd been to England and could speak English, Bengali and Hindi ...

"I didn't know that." Daphne's eyebrows shot up.

"Three thousand applicants," boomed Philip. "Most of them impossible. I short-listed some and interviewed them, but none of them had a clue. It's only for six weeks but I must find someone soon. We need to start our research ..."

Before I had time to register this amazing piece of luck, fingers were pointing firmly at me.

"There's the man for you. Fits the bill, everything you want." Daphne and her friends were exultant.

"Look that's your man. No need to go any further."

"Good God," said Philip.

Forget the future for six weeks. This was going to be fun.

And more than fun. Ten pounds a week was an enormous sum of money. On one pound ten shillings a week a man could pay the rent, maintain a wife and two children - and send the children to school.

And more than money. Respect. I felt equal to these men despite my race, something that hadn't happened in London or in Stuttgart. Not that Philip's big smile didn't hide the toughness peculiar to all directors. If he asked for a white elephant you'd have to find one. Directors didn't ask, they told. That was the first lesson.

The film was to be called Steel Goddess, a documentary about the building of a steel mill in the Durgapur jungle. We were returning to the very area where the tiger had padded across the road in front of me a quarter of a century before.

The eyes of that magnificent beast challenged me again and a thrill of anticipation ran through my body as we neared the end of our journey.

There was nothing to recognize. The jungle was no more, not a single tree.

In its place monstrous cooling towers soared to a terrific height and on the reddish earth below 10,000 people, the majority of them women, laboured with their hands. No need for huge tractors - the women carried the cement on their heads, for ten shillings a week. If they were skilled, they could earn 15 shillings.

A consortium of 12 British firms had got the contract to build the steel mill. At least ten square miles of my Durgapur jungle had been swallowed up by the 80 million pound project. Prime Minister Nehru wanted to catch up with the Western world. India needed steel for its railways and for other commodities, he said. She must be forward looking.

The work continued day and night. Sometimes we went off in the jeep at two in the morning to take the most fantastic shots. The huge cooling towers were lit by electric bulbs so powerful that you couldn't see the stars. The maze of temporary roads was well lit too, so the shadows that resulted were stark and frightening and the darkness beyond seemed even more profound.

Philip Donnellan was interested in the effect this monstrous undertaking would have on the villages round the area. He needed interviews with someone in a Bengali family who lived in a village and had a job on the site or the promise of a job once the mill was finished.

Dressed as a traditional Bengali in my loin cloth, finding the ideal family and being accepted was not too difficult. Because of my high caste they were obliged to let me in. The long footage of filming and the interviews meant badly needed cash, but I still wondered about the future of the 13-year-old daughter and her baby of three months.

The crew had a VIP officer's bungalow, English style, but with no running water. Being on site, the surroundings were stark, stripped of any trees, but with beautiful views in the distance of untouched jungle.

It was left to me to organize the running of the bungalow, engage the cook and the sweeper.

Both servants were Muslim. The cook, Mohammed, had a family of three who moved into the servants' quarters, and he made splendid curries. Milder ones had to be introduced for one member of the crew, Fred, who couldn't stand the heat.

One afternoon we came in late for lunch. The temperature was 45°C. Mohammed was acting oddly. The rice he brought was only warm, but that was not so bad in this heat. I let it pass. The lentils weren't warmed up at all. I told him to warm them.

"And you're a bit silly the way you're walking, aren't you?"

"*Suar ko bacha*. You son of a pig."

What! The worst insult an Indian can be given, especially from a servant.

Before I could get my breath back Mohammed had rushed into the kitchen, snatched the saucepan full of cold lentils and hurled it at my face.

God! Go for him! Mohammed was a very strong man but I was beside myself with rage. I dragged him outside and beat the hell out of him.

"You'll kill him. What are you doing?" Philip's voice barely impinged on my consciousness but I was dimly aware of someone trying to pull my victim away.

I got Mohammed on the floor, stood on his chest, blind with fury, unaware how I was hurting him.

"*Babu, babu.*"

Immediately Mohammed's wife started touching my feet it was all over. I was myself again, humiliated that I could have done such a thing. After all, the man was drunk.

The crew had never seen anything like it, didn't understand what had happened. The insult, I explained ... Philip took it all with good humour. Neither of us got the sack.

"Find me a buffalo and someone to wash it with mud."

Not a white elephant. Finding a water buffalo in the river was the easy part. But an Indian man or child to wash it?

Out of luck. The river was low in March, only knee deep. But how would I go about washing such a huge animal? My hands shook.

I needn't have worried. My buffalo was docile once it got to know me and it seemed to like being rubbed with mud. My bare back and bottom with only a rope round my waist, would appear in the film. Fame again.

We were mixing with the famous too. The Duke of Edinburgh was among the visitors to this amazing project. Once when he got crowded out, he and his bodyguard jumped into the jeep with Philip and me. "And what are you doing here?" he asked.

Another request from Philip. "Can you find some writing on a wall or something, political or poetical."

No difficulty this time. As if chalked up there on the wall just for me was a line from a poem by Rabindranath Tagore. Perfect: "Into that heaven of freedom, my Father, let my country awake."

It was from the Gitanjali. Back at home that wonderful work was waiting for me to discover all over again. Tagore was after all a son of Bengal - my Rabindra Lake honoured him. The book fell open at Gitanjali 13:

"The song that I came to sing remains unsung to this day.

I have spent my days in stringing and in unstringing my instrument.

The time has not come true, the words have not been rightly set; only there is the agony of wishing in my heart..."

What song had I really come to sing?

But there was no time to think about it. Daphne had been transferred to Delhi. "Why don't you come along? I can get you some more jobs - film crews usually come to Delhi and with your recommendation from Philip Donnellan ..."

She was right. John Williamson, director of documentary films for the BBC, wanted me to help with a piece on the old buildings in Amhedabad, north of Bombay.

Then there was Charles Wheeler, the correspondent who lived in Delhi with his wife Catherine, Daphne's friend. Charles had to phone in a broadcast three days a week and he needed a dogsbody. For six months carrying his heavy tape-recorder was my passport to the company of such people as Nehru, Eisenhower and Radhakrishnan, the great philosopher who was then President of India. Charles would edit the recordings and play them to London over the phone.

Sabrina had come with me to Delhi of course - she was about to be exchanged for a newer model. But one hot day I was on my bicycle, sailing quietly down a narrow road, enjoying the prospect of a few weeks off, money to spare, a completely blue sky, and a feeling that something was going to happen.

Up in the blue, a tiny dot, pivoting round. Probably 6000 feet up. Where had it come from?

My fall onto the dust was as if in slow motion. The bicycle and I had veered off the road and collided with a mango tree.

A *chai* wallah in his shack nearby burst out laughing.

"Stop laughing and make me a cup of tea. Not too much sugar please."

The mango tree towered above me, like the one I'd met Kalu in, like the ones we'd launched ourselves from in our efforts to fly, and above it the glider slowly got bigger and bigger, then disappeared behind the trees.

I picked myself up. "Why did it land there? Was it a forced landing?"

"Didn't you know?" said the *chai* wallah. "There's an airfield behind there."

An airfield, was there?

The tea in the little earthenware pot tasted extraordinarily good. Before it was finished my mind was made up. I would go to the airfield and enquire at the gliding club there. Just enquire.

CHAPTER 23

The airfield had been built during the war. Now it was surrounded by more recent buildings and only one side had a road. Bullock carts and bicycles waited behind a barrier when Dakotas came in to land.

"How many gliders?"

Five. Two for training and three for initial solo flights and advanced work.

"Subscription?"

One rupee.

"Are you sure you haven't flown before?" asked Chief Instructor Mr Pujji after a few flights.

"No, never."

As long as there were no solo flights, I was quite relaxed, my fear gone.

"Come on, you've had 13 flights. Off you go solo."

I grabbed his hand. "Please, please don't ask me that. Can't I fly with another instructor?"

"Good idea. Second opinion."

There were seven instructors in all and I went through the lot of them.

Each time, "Please don't ask me to go solo. I'll tell you when I'm ready. You can teach me advanced techniques."

Every day we watched the kites on the outskirts of the airfield. They stood around waiting for the sun to burn the earth and produce the thermals that would get them airborne effortlessly.

We would see them start up, not attempting to flap their wings, then sink down again. "No, not enough yet, chaps."

They'd walk around a bit, then settle down to wait. We too would watch and wait, perspiring in the heat.

At last, three feet off the ground they would spread their great dark wings, never flapping them, and start to circle, shooting upwards with lazy speed, a thousand feet in the twinkling of an eye. Then we would rush to the hangars, get out the gliders and follow their example, like little boys spreading our arms in their wake.

What did these creatures think of our bumbling efforts?

A clear blue sky, silent, so cool after the heat of the burning earth. Way below, the Jamuna River winding towards Agra, with life clustered about its banks. Alone at last, in a single-seater glider, and unafraid.

Alone? One of those magnificent creatures was soaring with me. Chil the kite flew very close, popped his head out from his shoulders, had a good look, then withdrew himself. He kept me company for nearly 15 minutes, way up at 4500 feet where kites don't normally fly, too high to spot their prey. He dropped out of sight once in a while, then followed me again, flying for the sheer pleasure of it, free in a vast sky.

My heart swelled inside me. This was what it was all about. It wasn't just a question of learning to fly, this was the feeling, the privilege I had to pass on.

It was getting too cold up there - unbelievable that people on the ground were sweltering in 40°C. When I pulled the spoilers out to lose the lift the noise of the airflow surprised my companion. But he kept on following, right down to 2000 feet, the edges of his wings fringed like spread fingers.

The kite and I, were we such very different creatures in Lord Shiva's sight? And people - what should there be to divide us, we who live together in the heat under a vast sky? Try explaining these thoughts to Mohanlal, Daphne's sweeper.

It was impossible to live with Daphne in Chanakyapuri, the select area for all the diplomats in Delhi, without my being her employee. So I was her driver, with my room upstairs in the roof. I led a kind of double life, only guessed at by Mohamed, the Kashmiri cook.

Mohanlal the sweeper had no suspicions. Mohanlal couldn't read or write but he loved to hear the stories of the Ramayana - the capture of Sita, the monkey god Hanuman flying to her rescue ... Kalu and I had launched ourselves from the mango tree telling such stories.

Mohanlal would not sit on a chair with me however much I asked. He sat on the bare floor. He was the lowest caste, a sweeper, and I was so high caste, how could he sit with me?

It was only an accident of birth, I told him. He hadn't had the opportunity for education, that was all. We were both equal.

"How can we be the same?"

He swept with dignity, slow steady strokes, his eyes untroubled. For a moment as I watched they were my hands, lighter brown, around the broom, in another time and place.

"James Ivory has asked me whether I know of anybody to help him with his BBC documentary, Gateway to Delhi." Daphne was smiling. "I told him I did."

I was hired for three months, from January 1960.

The Red Fort in Old Delhi stood on the west bank of the Jamuna river, its high redstone walls enclosing marble palaces. The women dyeing cloth bright scarlet in front of the walls had given us some marvellous shots but James Ivory - Jim - had seen something else. He'd zoomed in to a beggar playing his two-stringed instrument.

"Toon, come here. Look through this camera. His toes are dropping off."

The beggar had leprosy. Jim, who normally displayed an almost Indian serenity, was severely shocked. Back at the hotel, work was impossible. The gentle smile had disappeared and the light grey eyes looked haunted.

"Find a home for that beggar."

How could I tell him that we couldn't bridge the gap, that he'd go back to being a beggar, that he'd always be a beggar? Just as Mohanlal's destiny was to sweep, his was to beg. I knew I couldn't say this. I would have to do as I was asked.

At the leprosy colony they told me to see Group Captain Leonard Cheshire, who came to Delhi in the winter months. I couldn't wait to meet this inspiring man who embodied so many of my longings. I'd read about him as a pilot, surviving his terrible accident, and about the conversion to Christianity which prompted his wonderful work.

A skinny man with kind eyes, in a blue-green bush shirt and shorts, he seemed to have the knack of giving two different people his whole attention at the same time. While he talked to me, he was also attending to a man with hardly any fingers, only four foot tall, who was jumping up and down in front of him.

I brought our beggar to Leonard Cheshire. But about a month later he was sitting in his place in front of the walls, playing his *esraj*.

And my destiny? Would I come back to flying again and again, or was I to work with my less fortunate brothers, like the Jurgens and Leonard Cheshires of this world?

I'd seen the Jamuna River wind towards Agra from the air. Now we were to film it flowing past the Taj Mahal, the marigolds of the dead glowing on its muddy grey surface, the buffalo wallowing in its shallows.

Jim hadn't cared how long it took to get permission to climb up one of the ornamental minarets at the four corners of the Taj Mahal. It took three weeks.

Even on the day, everything moved slowly as usual. Although we'd started early it was late morning before we climbed the 364 steps. Plenty of time to wonder at the white marble monument to love with its intricate patterns of semi-precious stones, reflected in the watercourse. Time to spot the brilliant colours of a kingfisher.

We were climbing the first minaret to the right of the entrance, Jim holding the camera and I the tripod. At 200 feet we squeezed out onto a tiny space enclosed by a very low parapet. The sensation was extraordinary. Our perch was so small and nothing else was joined to it, or even at the same height. It was as if we were suspended in mid-air, stationary in a small plane.

The view was fantastic. The sun shone on the white marble of the main monument, not as magically as at sunrise or as dreamily as at sunset but the effect was still impressive.

Was the kingfisher still perched above the watercourse?

"I'm going to have a look down," I said. Then nothing.

When I came round I was lying cramped on the floor and Jim was bending over me.

"Thank God," he said. "Lucky I was there to grab you. You fainted clean away. Now I've seen a white Indian."

This was my first experience of vertigo. It doesn't happen in planes.

"Just be careful. Don't look down."

The minaret had been open to the public until 1945 but there were so many suicides they had to shut it up. Suicides or cases of vertigo?

Next we were given permission to climb on to the roof of the main monument, via a precarious series of ladders. From here we could marvel at the vastness of the place and wonder at how they had managed to build it, even with 20,000 slaves.

"Do you realize you and I are the only two people ever to come up here?"

Jim was forgetting the workers who had to maintain it, but the feeling was exhilarating all the same.

We stared across the Jamuna River at the Red Fort of Agra on the opposite bank. The day had yielded a few seconds' worth of panoramic view for the film and a life-long memory for us.

My work with Jim was coming to an end, but he wanted to visit Benares, to see the pilgrims by the ghats on the Ganges. This was a stroke of luck as Baba was in Benares. We stayed in a hotel and struggled through the crowded streets to see him.

He'd given up smoking and drinking and looked quite emaciated, the ghost of my father.

"The BBC may be sending me to London on a job for a while, Baba."

Baba smiled. The much respected BBC. That had to be good, he would be thinking. Perhaps his younger son wasn't doing so badly after all. And of course they would send him back to India when the assignment was over.

London, but this time with a job - and a good one - already organized. My wings were beginning to lift all over again.

"*Takur tomakay dekben*. God be with you."

I was going with Baba's blessing.

CHAPTER 24

"No, we can't take your scooter. It's not possible."

My apparently invalid passport had already caused a stir. It had been renewed in 1959 but the nine looked like a four - a problem to thoroughly excite everybody. Now they wanted a bribe to take Sabrina Mark II.

I stood my ground. They looked me up and down.

"Oh, let the poor bugger go," said one suddenly.

The very last passenger, I joined the hundreds already on board the boat from Bombay to Genoa.

"Where's my scooter?"

"It's all your fault," said the Chief Steward. "You should have got your passport written properly. Holding everyone up."

"Where is my - "

But there it was, swinging across in a high crane, the name Sabrina clearly in view. Relief. As soon as it was down, a high pitched whistle sounded from the four corners, the horn boomed and the propellers churned water noisily. The boat set off at a snail's pace.

Now I could observe my companions for the next 14 days. Rubber-slippers stood out from the rest - I'd noticed him before we boarded. A white man with a red, intelligent face, his cotton shirt hung over brown and white checked cotton trousers and his slippers were made of motor car tyre. We seemed to gravitate towards each other.

He'd walked from Germany to India, and I knew what that meant ...

But he was returning a rather disillusioned man. "You see this scar?"

It was the spiritual India which had so fascinated and drawn him but he'd not wanted to join an ashram and stay in one place, so, puzzlingly harassed by the people he admired, he meditated alone. One day he sat under a banyan tree in a village near Madras. And the children stoned him. And left a scar.

We stood on our heads on the boat and talked about life. We enjoyed ourselves. They couldn't stop us joining in the dancing once I'd lent him one of my ties and a pair of shoes. Who cared if the ladies gave us a wide berth?

The train was confining after the boat. I was invited to arrive in London on 5th May to learn from the team's coverage of Princess Margaret's wedding but trouble at the German-Belgian border sent me back to Cologne to get a visa from the Belgian embassy. So I hit London on 6th May, exactly five years since I'd left it.

"Hampstead," wrote Baba. "How wonderful. Do they still have horse-drawn tramcars?"

The railway company had sent him to England in 1923. The journey had taken 52 days.

No horse-drawn tramcars trundled along tree-lined Fitzjohn's Avenue in 1960, but my top-floor flat at 114 was wonderful all the same.

My only worry was Daphne. She'd returned to London before me, ill with the dysentry which had weakened her all the time she was in India. Now she'd been transferred to King's Cross Hospital, for investigation by the London School of Hygiene and Tropical Medicine. The sight of her shocked me - she'd lost so much weight, her hair was really short and her eyes seemed to fill her gaunt face. There was nothing I could do except visit.

My job kept me busy. The first film to be researched was "Coventry Kids", a documentary about multi-racial life, explosive in a positive way. I got out of the bus at Coventry's Pool Meadow one sunny afternoon with no clue as to how to find what Philip Donnellan wanted - a pub run by a local person with a black man playing a guitar in an alleyway, white prostitutes throwing darts, Jamaicans and Englishmen bent over dominoes and an Indian who worked in a factory. Add an Irishman for good measure.

But first I had to find accommodation with an Indian or Jamaican family.

It was hot, my case was heavy, there were rows and rows of houses broken only by snack bars and traffic lights. A Jamaican gave me an address but when I knocked on the door, "No room for you here." My knees were weak from walking. I asked the first Indian I saw.

This Punjabi nodded his head. We went through his kitchen door and met the eyes of a very tall woman in salwar and kamiz. "Namastay."

I thought she had a motherly smile and I was right. A ten-month-old baby girl lay on the filthiest couch in England. The room was in real pandemonium - razor blades, broken mirror and half a comb on the mantelpiece, nappies everywhere, cigarette butts on the floor, all mixed up with the smell of spices out of a pot. I was no longer a foreigner in England.

The second film, "White Chalk", was set in Stoke-on-Trent. Here I had to find an old man who'd been a potter since youth, and that was easy. I had to see whether he'd lost any toes because of the wheel, but my potter had lost a thumb.

And it was I who was forced to bite the rifle cartridge, rumoured to be greased with the fat of cows and pigs, which started the 1857 mutiny against British rule in "The Lords of India," and my brown hands - close-up shot - that played chess against the prince.

We went to the British Museum to fit me out as an Indian sepoy in trousers, waistcoat with brass buttons, and white dog collar. I researched in the Indian library near Holborn, and then we went to Sandhurst. They were right - the resemblance to Lucknow was amazing.

Meanwhile a sequence was shot of a child in the arms of its mother in Bombay, begging. The child had been blinded for the purpose. This gave a false impression, said the Indian Government, it was very rare. A ban was put on any documentary films being made by the BBC in India.

I'd realized by now that my experience in England was intended to equip me better for working with the BBC in India.

"Of course we'll let you know if the ban is lifted, but in the meantime ..." The fare back to India and a handshake and that was it.

August 1960. No intention of going home without a job. This was my second chance. Besides I was still living in style in Fitzjohn's Avenue. All my debts were paid off and I still felt rich. The ban would soon be lifted, or there would be some other job with the BBC. Why worry? Hanuman and Lord Shiva were on my side.

Everyone loved my parties. Why stop them? Daphne was better - she'd become so exhausted with being poked about in hospital with no results that I'd said, "Well why don't you leave?" and she'd walked out. Her parents lived nearby to help and her health had gradually improved. She enjoyed my parties.

Dada stayed with me when his firm sent him to England, so did Phil from Australia, still infected with wanderlust. So did the Commissioner of Police of Calcutta, who ran up huge telephone bills and cost the earth to entertain - I couldn't ask for any money from Baba's friend, could I? No-one realized the money was running out - and nothing was coming in.

No sign of the ban being lifted. A feeling of unease. The rent for Fitzjohn's Avenue was still eight guineas a week, my income nil, the BBC money quickly disappearing. A niggle of regret. Couldn't I have used that money to learn to fly?

When I had these thoughts, Baba's eyes still haunted me, not calm and full of blessing as I'd last seen them in Benares but dark, angry and sad.

Perhaps I should join Jurgen in Stuttgart - we were still in close contact. I had to do something with my life and working with handicapped children would be so worthwhile.

But I couldn't make the decision, couldn't get rid of the urge to fly that kept fighting through my fear into the front of my mind. So I stalled.

The money had practically run out. The landlady turned a blind eye when I let out two of my three rooms, one to a Bengali couple and one to an American boy who lived on his nerves and his multitudes of pills. But even this wouldn't keep me solvent for long.

I made enquiries with the RAF but I was just too old. Relief perhaps, but now I began to panic. I had to get a job, any job, to make ends meet before I decided what to do.

I became cook's assistant at the Moulin Rouge in Finchley Road, starting at eight in the morning. Downstairs had to be cleaned first because the restaurant opened at nine. The restaurant, with some 24 tables, nicely decorated and quite easy to clean, was presided over by a photograph of the Queen and the Duke of Edinburgh.

The nightclub upstairs was next to clean. During the week the mess was bearable but at weekends it was unbelievably disgusting. I worked weekends to pick up double money.

In the first week I found ten sixpences on the restaurant floor and another ten upstairs. I handed them over to my boss. Mr Martin was playing the piano to himself, half drunk.

"Ali," - he always called me Ali - "remember something. When you pick up a hundred pounds' worth of sixpences give them all to me. If there are less than a hundred pounds' worth, you keep them."

I lasted five weeks.

"You son of a pig."

What! The chief cook, a Hungarian, probably hadn't meant anything by this form of address but it was the worst insult for an Indian. My honour was at stake. I snatched up my broom and advanced towards the cook. He took fright at the savage fury in my face and made a quick retreat.

Nothing was said about this incident, but my anger at the next one was even greater and not misplaced.

The cook's son picked up a mouse and calmly put a candle to its face, watching it writhe.

I hit his hand and walked out.

"It is horrible," said Mr Martin. "But well, mice are pests."

"Kill them outright, yes. But there's no need to be so cruel."

"Yes, but that's life, isn't it, Ali? Don't leave your job over it."

"Give me my wages, Mr Martin, and I'll think about it."

I wanted a job in the fresh air. I knew I couldn't keep the flat on much longer even by staying at the Moulin Rouge. I was getting desperate.

The only permanent job I could find was a sweeper with Hampstead Borough Council - I was to be number 6748.

CHAPTER 25

My name changed from Ali to John. All Indians were called
John then. I was added to the roll call, "John!", at 6.55 am in
Rosslyn Hill, when 20 or so sweepers with their barrows
answered the register before setting out on their beat at seven.
Flask Walk, Hampstead Heath, Primrose Hill, Swiss Cottage
... The beat to be avoided went along Fitzjohn's Avenue.

I watched people eating bananas and throwing down the skins
to join the rest of the filth on the pavement - not the shiny
spotless surface in which I'd once, in my innocence, expected
to see my face. A coating of grime everywhere. How was I
going to stick this job?

But the sun shone and leaf shadows danced on that tree- lined
pavement. I looked up - the dusty green leaves were beginning
their transformation, hinting at the glorious shades of autumn,
and above them fluffy cumulus clouds were building up in a
blue, blue sky. It wasn't so bad.

Then there was Taffy. Sometimes when our beats crossed I
looked up and saw Taffy, his tall and powerful frame silhouetted
against the sky.

"How're you doing, John?" he'd growl.

He looked the kind of man you'd run from in the dark. His
manners were rough and the ugliness of his face fascinated me
at first, until I got to know him and he was just Taffy, the
kindest, wisest man in the world.

His eyes were enormous under the tangled grey brows, the
right eyebrow slightly higher than the left, giving him a lopsided
appearance.   His nose was bent to one side and quite a few
front teeth were missing, the gaps barely covered by thick
lips. Taffy had wrinkles all over his face, even on his bent
nose. He would have beaten the world record for wrinkles.
His dishevelled grey hair, which he cut himself, was all over
the place and his complexion was red.

"Drinking is so good for you. You drink, and then it's
cheerful you are. Come on, John, we go drinking now."

He seemed to change when we were alone and he was surprisingly articulate. He must have read a lot even though he couldn't focus very well with his right eye. He filled me in on the class system, which struck a chord.

"We're going to write a play about it, me and Paddy. Make you laugh, make you think, it will."

When Paddy joined us and they got excited about their play or about putting the world to rights, my eyes flicked from one to the other, fascinated - it was like watching a game of table-tennis. I barely understood a word.

Not all the members of the team were so articulate. Another Irishman, Shaun, worried me from the first day. He was a filthy old boy who never talked to anyone, just swept with his head down. The others said he had something missing.

I felt compelled to take him to Fitzjohn's Avenue, offer him a bath and feed him. For a brief hour, clean, transformed, eating ravenously, he let the shutters down. Without expressing gratitude exactly, there was a warmth in him I'd never seen before. He talked about all the things he might have done. And about his wife.

"When Marie died," he said softly, "that finished me off."

And then he was out in the street again and he slipped away, withdrew into himself, silent, head down, as if he'd never allowed a glimpse of the Shaun inside.

I suddenly thought of the beggar in Delhi sitting back at the same spot with his toes eaten away. I needed Taffy.

I looked forward to our beats crossing.

"Why would you be picking up those grasses there?" Taffy watched as I pulled at the weeds poking up between the pavement and the wall. "Beautiful things, they are."

"I'll be told off by the foreman if I leave them."

"That's your trouble. You should think for yourself. We're not paid to get rid of weeds. As it is we're trodden on. In a job like this ..."

"I beg your pardon. It's a good job we're doing."

I was proud now to push my barrow and my personal broom was jealously guarded - I'd painted my name on it.

"What are you doing here?"

Three well-dressed young Indians stopped me outside Belsize Park tube station.

"*Apni aykanay kee korchen.*" I said in Bengali. "I don't know English."

"You come to England and sweep the streets. Why are you doing this low caste work when we can see from your face you are high caste?"

I kept my temper for a while.

"People like you shame India. You make a bad name for us."

I lost it, snatched up my broom, threatened to swipe, my face dark.

"You three get the hell out of here quickly," I said in English. "You should be ashamed of yourselves. You come here and spend thousands of your parents' rupees, and you are the people who sully the name of India. I know all about the likes of you and I don't want to see you again - ever."

Crowds walked by, pretending not to look.

"*Ahmra jantam nah.* We did not know." Abject, shattered faces.

"Look, none of you can speak good English anyway."

I turned my back on them and continued sweeping.

I was happy with my job, but it didn't pay for a flat in Fitzjohn's Avenue.

"This is it," I told the landlady at last. I was penniless. Sabrina Mark II had already been sold for a song, having gently fallen apart.

We found a room together in Kilburn, Taffy and I - he hadn't been happy with his lodgings. It wasn't much of a room. The little basin leaked, not that there was water to fill it for much of the time - there always seemed to be burst pipes or leakages somewhere in the system. Taffy used to wet the bed and I would change the sheet for him, cursing the leaking basin which was all we had to wash in.

Taffy was so powerful he could lift me with two hands, but he supported me too with his spirit - he had a different, strong way of looking at life, a father and a friend to me.

The sad child deep inside the fierce exterior only added to his power. I half worshipped him for his ideas.

October. Sometimes the sky was grey and rain lashed the pavements, sending everyone scuttling past me, splashing in the puddles. Sometimes the sky was blue and the cumulus clouds dissolved and reformed like my changing ideas of the future. If only I could get under those clouds, I thought, I could glide so far. I could only hear the swishing noise of the air past my glider, hardly noticed the people almost colliding with my barrow down below.

The beat along Fitzjohn's Avenue didn't worry me any more. I passed the jutting triangle of red brick without a glance.

But it was in that same street I caught sight of Catherine, wife of Charles Wheeler in different, Delhi days. Suddenly aware of my scruffy peaked cap and dirty old overcoat - there was no uniform supplied - I pulled my cap over my face, shrugged into myself and bent low over the dog's dirt I was shovelling up. I had a scarf over my nose because of the smell.

"Who are you hiding from?"

Catherine grabbed me and hugged me and pushed the cap back off my face.

"Catherine, I want a bath."

She went away and did her shopping until my lunch break, then I hid my barrow and went with her up Holly Hill to have a bath.

That was the first of many visits to the house in Holly Hill, enjoying the company of Catherine and her friends - John Freeman whom I'd admired in his Face to Face programme, prominent intellectuals such as the Huxleys, and of course Daphne. But I always went home to Taffy. And my broom was always at the ready for 6.55 am.

Usually I spent my lunch breaks alone in a pub - different pub for different beats, sitting down with a pint of bitter, writing in my diary. Once I was sitting outside in the sun when two men with bowlers and umbrellas walked past.

One of them pointed his umbrella at his companion. "Look you ..."

The other shouted back.

Oh my God, we're going to have problems here, I thought. I got up and left my pint of bitter, prepared to intervene, but the publican came out to me.

"I've seen you writing. You're a quiet man, an Indian. These two are English gentlemen and that's the way they talk, shouting and pointing umbrellas. Friends call each other names. So don't worry, you will understand the culture when you've been here a while."

Would I? And how long could I stay here anyway?

Leaves fell from the trees - all the shades of yellow, orange, brown and scarlet. A privilege to sweep them every day from early morning until late afternoon, to be under them as they floated down, to feel them round my feet and follow their antics with my broom. Taffy thought so too.

Our beats crossed in Primrose Hill. We danced up and down on the leaves, shuffling in them like children, shouting for joy. A stiff breeze shook the trees and more leaves broke free.

"Catch one and your fortune's made, so it is," growled Taffy. His tall clumsy frame lurched this way and that, his outstretched hands grabbing in vain at the air. What should have been ungainly had a grace of its own. In India we'd have attracted a crowd, perhaps been applauded. But here people walked by pretending not to look.

I held out my hands, happy to be there, not even trying to catch. It was a plane leaf, reddish like a maple and it seemed to be drawn to my hand like iron to a magnet. It lay there perfect, stuck to my palm.

Taffy's mouth dropped open. Then he leapt in the air. "You lucky bastard. You can never go wrong after this."

I pressed the leaf in my journeybook and that night I had a dream.

Another Toon stood over me, looking down at me as Taffy might have done.

"You've got to make up your mind. What are you going to do? The only thing is to look about you. Relax, enjoy yourself. Why take yourself so seriously?"

The next morning was beautiful and I had my favourite beat - Hampstead Ponds to Spaniards Inn. St Paul's with its mosque-like dome down in the hazy distance could have been the set for a nostalgic film. A dog ran across the coarse brown grass, fur in little wet points beneath its belly. Hampstead Ponds. I remembered landing by those ponds in the dream I'd had staying with Fay and Phil, the first time in London, before the snow. I'd forgotten that dream until now - I'd been flying with my arms outstretched over unknown places. Where had I started from?

It was a long walk to Spaniards Inn. Bubbles of cloud began forming against a background of real blue. How lovely it would be up in that sky in a glider with only the noise of the wind.

There was something newly familiar about that walk and I began to wonder what it would have looked like from above ...

The tug of war inside me continued for several days. I asked the Toon from my dream, should I join Jurgen? Could I cope with hundreds and thousands of handicapped people? It wouldn't be the same as just one or two. You have to devote yourself completely to what you want, he said. However selfish it might be, I just couldn't devote myself to Jurgen's work. I knew really what I wanted to do. Why try to hide it, then? asked the dream Toon. You have to fly.

As soon as the decision had been made, I knew it was right, in spite of my horoscope, in spite of Baba, in spite of everything. There was a tremendous feeling of relief and my barrow danced along the streets. Lord Shiva would be on my side.

"There's better you are now, John?" growled Taffy, and took me for a drink.

"It's right to the top you'll go whatever you do, lucky bastard, with that leaf."

Thanks to Catherine, and Daphne's father, who vouched for my character, I took two weeks out from sweeping to work in the Post Office before Christmas.

Primrose Hill, Chalk Farm, delivering parcels - until seven in the evening on Christmas Eve. It was often dark when I passed the church with the deep porch and delivered to the house where I'd lived with Phil and Fay, where I'd had the flying dream. Sometimes there were ghosts.

It was late when I got back to Taffy and our Kilburn room.

"What do you think you're doing here? You must be mad. I've had a hell of a job to find you."

My brother was waiting for me. Dada's firm had sent him to London again and he was expecting to stay with me in Fitzjohn's Avenue as before. He couldn't understand how I'd become destitute after enjoying such a lifestyle. He'd been told I worked as a sweeper and tracked me down through Hampstead Borough Council.

"You shouldn't be living in this awful room with a man who wets the bed."

Mind your own business, Dada, was my silent reply.

"And you shouldn't be doing a low caste job."

"Baba never gave me any money to do what I want to do."

"All right, here you are. I'll give you a hundred pounds."

"I don't want that money."

"Here you are, you go and start flying. I'll make it right with Baba."

I could have hugged him. At last, I had permission and my conscience was free. Baba was already very ill. Dada, as the eldest son, was taking his place and had actually told me to go and fly.

There was nothing to hold me back now. Unlike Mohanlal in Delhi, sweeping was not my destiny.

Dada returned to Calcutta. The gliding magazine came to me through Francis Huxley and it was there I saw the advertisement. I'd got to know Francis through Catherine and he'd taken my sweeper's job for one day, just to see what it was like.

Now I was giving it up for ever, not just for one day or two weeks. But there was Taffy.

"When you go away, when you separate from someone you love, you've gained, not lost. You're doing the right thing, you are."

But the morning after I left, I imagined Taffy standing in the dark with the others for the roll call. I imagined them all going their own ways with their barrows and their brooms, and Taffy with his, watching the sun rise on another day, and I hid my face.

CHAPTER 26

"Sure you won't ride her? It's a fair stretch - take you a good two hours. And she's very placid, you know."

I didn't expect to meet a man on the road with a horse to spare. The stranger sat erect on his chestnut mare, gesturing at a second mare roped by his side. The road stretched bleakly into the cold distance. It was tempting, and if the offered animal hadn't been white ...

Who had persuaded me to ride that white horse in Kashmir without a saddle? The "gentle" beast had gone crazy and bolted off the road. I'd vowed never to ride again. And today was not a day for taking risks.

"Well if you're sure then, the Golden Pot public house and turn left. Good luck. And remember me to the Chowringhee." His breath puffed into the wintry air.

A friendly salute and he was gone, another ex-serviceman who knew Calcutta from the war. The horses trotted away until the sound of their hooves faded and the rider was a mere speck.

Walking in the cold was hardly a new experience and six miles was nothing with such an end in sight. Wind tugged at the grass on the field beside the road but there were no leaves twirling, not in January.

Taffy was right, I was a lucky bastard. I closed my fingers over Dada's roll of notes, a hard lump in my pocket. It was only three weeks since he'd given me that money and here I was making for Lasham, the largest gliding centre in Europe.

Alton station, teeming with ex-servicemen, was well behind me, the Golden Pot and a pint of bitter not far ahead. A startled crow burst into the grey sky, cawing, flapping indignantly. I had to get to the interview on time. Nothing must go wrong.

The winch-driver's job wouldn't get me airborne again, but it would put me in the right place to make my dreams come true. Then it would be up to me.

By the time I reached the Golden Pot my battered cardboard suitcase was beginning to stretch my arm, even though all it contained was a change of clothes - I'd sold everything else back in Hampstead.

On the last leg of the journey, with a warming pint inside me, I saw the first glider rise steeply into the grey sky, then another and another. Each new flight sent a shiver through my body.

Soon the airfield itself came into view - ex-RAF buildings scattered round the edge of a huge grassy plain, flattened by dull sky. My stomach was churning. I had to get this job. There was no going back.

A mid-grey cat, all fluff, walked sedately across my path, stopped half-way and swivelled its head round, owl-like, to stare. Its eyes were a strange bluish-green.

A white glider climbed into the sky ahead of me, the winch still out of sight. The glider released and the little coloured parachute floated the cable safely to the ground. Elated, I made my way to the control tower.

The interview took place in an ante-room off the rather tatty clubroom, a corner next to the parachute cupboard. My interviewers appraised me in a shrewd but friendly manner across the table. The surface was almost bare apart from coffee cups - and one of the saucers was chipped. My scruffy clothes didn't feel so out of place after all.

"Have you any experience of winch driving, Mr Ghose?"

"Of course I have." (At least I'd seen the barrage balloon winches with their yellow rollers during the war and I'd watched similar ones being driven in Delhi.)

"Why do you want the job?"

"So that I can pay for gliding lessons."

"Have you done any gliding?"

"Only once or twice, when I was a winch driver in Delhi." (No need to say I'd been solo. My log book was lost anyway.)

"Why are you so interested in flying?"

"I've always wanted to fly. My father wouldn't give me money so I rode to London on a scooter."

"From where?"

"From Calcutta. To learn to fly." (No need to say when.)

"If we gave you the job you'd work five days a week and at weekends you could start flying. But you'd have to become a member of the Kent and Surrey Flying Club."

"That's all right. My brother has given me a hundred pounds to start."

"OK. We'll come back to you."

"But I can't afford to go back now. The money is for gliding."

"Have you got everything with you then? Haven't you got a home in London?"

"Well no. It's all in my suitcase here."

Soon the terrible wait was over. The job was mine. The battered case and I entered our new home - a corner in one of the ex-airforce bunk houses near the control tower.

There were two bunk houses - Fritz and the Ritz - squat, grey concrete, with badly fitting windows of small square panes. Each building boasted 16 bunks, used by members at weekends.

They gave me six army blankets to combat the January cold. Life was wonderful. I had a job, at £3 15s a week, to start the following Monday.

Winch driving at Lasham

That gave me one week to find out everything about the Clayton winch. I couldn't afford to make any mistakes.

"Take up slack." I watched the driver high up in the cabin ease in the throttle, taking up the cable slack slowly.

"All out!" The yellow flag signalled and the glider accelerated quickly and smoothly. It wouldn't be as easy as it looked to keep the glider at 45 or 50 mph airspeed all the way up until it released but my own gliding experience would help me judge the tension.

Glider after glider raced towards the winch and over my head like great winged dolphins rising to the surface from the deep sea bed. I breathed deeply.

In Delhi there'd been only one two-seater glider and three single-seaters. Here there was a hangar for 90 gliders with more of them outside, protected from the weather in their white coffins. There was plenty of room on this flat plain with the Surrey countryside falling away from it. A wide concrete runway ran from east to west, also used by Dan Air jets brought in for repair at the Maintenance Department in the south-west corner.

My spirit lifted with every launch. For half a day boss Bob Linton had taken me through my paces. Now I knew how to prepare the winch each morning, operate it, maintain and repair the cables. Soon I was in business, winching, watching and waiting for the weekend.

At night I put on the old flying suit they'd given me and arranged the army blankets, two below me on the mattress and four on top - no such luxuries as sheets. I held the heavy blankets off my chest - I weighed only nine stone - by fixing two wooden pegs, half an inch in diameter, by my head. The wind whistled through the broken window by my bunk. Probably I dreamt of flying, but I slept too soundly to remember, so motionless that in the morning the pegs hadn't moved.

"Come on, Toon. You fly and show me what you can do."

Derek Piggott, Chief Flying Instructor at Lasham, fascinated me. A rather short man, he seemed to have boundless energy, but always time to smile and wave a hand. His hands were large in proportion to his body, and very strong - he could even bend the piano wire they sometimes used for towing gliders on the runway.

"Now, show me what you can do."

Daisy, a T21B, was waiting at the launch point.

I was back in the cockpit again. It felt like coming home. Life was wonderful.

"Are you sure you haven't flown before?"

"I've been up a few times."

"But are you sure you haven't flown yourself?"

"No, no." (Stuttgart? Delhi? Another world. I wasn't going solo again until I'd learnt all I wanted from these instructors.)

A legend was beginning. The crazy Indian who'd come to London from Calcutta on a scooter to learn to fly was a natural. He would make unprecedented progress.

Every night I slept deeply, a tired and happy man.

"God, this blanket feels hard."

It was early morning, at the end of January, a fortnight after I'd arrived. Something was wrong. The wooden pegs were still in position but the blanket was stiff to touch and so, so cold. The silence was somehow deeper.

Only one way to find out what had happened. As I threw the blankets off, white flakes showered onto the concrete floor. What ...?

Outside the door I stopped, drew breath sharply. A white, fantastic, exciting world. Trees, grass, caravans, buildings all covered in white, tangy beauty. I'd never seen such a thick frost before. Wonderful. I threw my arms in the air and ran towards the clubhouse kitchen.

Wham! The world slipped from beneath me, like the bolting white horse. I lay on the cold crystals, rubbing my backside and marvelling at the skid marks left by my feet.

Twenty yards away at the kitchen door, Cookie was laughing fit to burst. She was a huge woman with a big smile, who came in from the nearby village of Herriard. In exchange for food I gave her a hand scrubbing floors or washing dishes in the evening or first thing in the morning. She had no paid help in the winter months and was glad of mine.

Her body still shook as she gave me my breakfast.

"So funny." She wiped her eyes.

By the end of the week all Lasham was laughing at my first encounter with a thick frost.

When it was too cold at night I crept across to the clubhouse and slept in the bar on a bench in the fireplace. A fluffy grey hot water bottle was provided - Min the cat. Min's bluish green eyes so close to mine stared with lazy affection, and her soft purring lulled me to sleep.

In the morning there was the cold water tap outside bunkhouse Fritz to brave, my only means of washing. Sometimes no courage was needed as there wasn't even a trickle - the tap was completely frozen up.

By the end of February the legend was beginning to grow. Solo after 15 or 16 launches? Who was this Indian? There weren't many Indians around then anyway, so I could hardly be missed. The dream was beginning to come true. Here I could learn to be truly airborne, push myself to the limit.

But here too, the dream had grown. However well I learnt to fly that wasn't going to be enough. I wanted to give this power, this freedom, to as many people as I could. I had to become an instructor, and a good one. It seemed a formidable aim.

In the meantime there was a problem of a different sort. By the end of February I desperately needed a bath. I didn't like to mention my unsavoury predicament and there was no Catherine to rescue me this time.

Or was there?

Six-year-old Janet, my confidante, Janet with her straight brown hair, cheeky eyes and rosy cheeks, told her mother. Ann Welch was a big name in gliding. At Lasham she instructed instructors and was chairman of the panel of examiners. She came up to me with a beautiful smile.

"Toon, is this true you can't have a bath? Janet says you haven't had a bath for six weeks."

What bliss in the Welch bath. I soaked in it for an hour, dried myself on the huge fluffy Welch towel, dressed in pyjamas belonging to Ann's husband twice my size, and enjoyed an English meal.

For once I didn't feel so bad about Daphne visiting me for the day, although she never seemed to mind my neglected state and always encouraged my dreams.

Spring came to Lasham. The woods across the road turned a fresh green. Little spots of wild colour appeared in the grass, fat bees hovered, and up above fluffy cumulus clouds chased across the sky. Spring warmed into summer, primroses and bluebells gave way to buttercups and clover, Lasham buzzed with activity.

On weekdays everyone was gliding. I launched one after the other, longing to be airborne myself, longing to be playing in the sky, experimenting with the beauty of it, exploring my soul, pushing at the frontiers, allowing myself to be swallowed up by the sheer wonder of it.

I'd flown solo not only in Daisy but also in the other T21Bs, Rudolf and Fanny, and in Eagles and Olympias. I'd had my first thrilling aerotow in a single-seater back in March, and at the end of April I'd graduated from the Olympia to the faster Skylark, the "hot ship".

The best instructors had brought me to a high standard in all sorts of skills in the sky - except soaring. There just hadn't been the opportunity to soar long enough or high enough. And without such experience it would be impossible to gain any qualifications, let alone learn to become an instructor. Frustration.

Dada's money had run out within a couple of months. A winch cost me two shillings and six pence - half the normal rate. An aerotow which would take me higher and give me more chance of finding thermals would have cost me 15 shillings.

But even money wasn't the biggest problem, thanks to the bar jar.

In the evenings I worked upstairs behind the club bar and was often offered drinks. More than two and I would be dancing with the customers, incapable of serving them. "Where's my beer?" So I refused the drinks.

But there was a genius at Lasham. "Don't be so stupid Toon, have the money instead, to go towards your launches. Put a jar under the counter."

A pint cost sixpence, a launch five times that.

"If the same guy offers you the money twice," continued the genius. "Put it in the jar."

The idea soon caught on. I felt rich.

But being able to pay for launches wasn't enough. It was no guarantee that I'd get the chance to soar, even in good weather. At weekends the order for launches was drawn from a hat and somehow I always seemed to be unlucky. I was getting hardly any experience in soaring at all.

The frustration drove me crazy. Something so simple was thwarting my aim and there didn't seem much I could do about it. Recklessly, I made things worse.

"I'm flying an Olympia tomorrow, Maimie," I said to one of the girls. "And I'm going to touch your hair with my wing tip on the launch point."

In the morning there was Maimie helping to take up the slack as usual and my boast in the bar came back to me. Why not? I misjudged and she fell over, laughing.

Half a dozen instructors witnessed the event.

Grounded.

Olympia

CHAPTER 27

"Please, please, give me a bit of thermal."

I'd been allowed up again, but so far there'd still been little chance of soaring.

It was six o'clock in the evening and a farmer had started burning some stubble. Up in the Skylark I scratched away for some lift, hoping the weak thermal would get stronger. "Please, God," I begged.

I managed to rise a little, turning sharply, then sank lower and lower to below 400 feet. Suddenly I caught the lift. Fantastic.

Up and up, soaring to 2000 feet. A couple of joyous loops and some wing-overs to salute the June evening. For 40 minutes I played in the sky. And then landed.

Half a dozen instructors were waiting.

"Come to the launch point."

"What have I done?"

"We'll tell you what you've done. You've broken all the rules. You were soaring too low, stopped everyone else from being launched. You make a decision at minimum 500 feet."

Grounded.

After a few days an instructor flew with me. Nothing wrong with my flying, so off I went again.

I soared up to 4000 feet, effortlessly, underneath a cloud - and somehow got sucked up in it. I was everywhere and nowhere, engulfed in a thick fog, blind to everything except the hail that was hitting the glass, terrified, exhilarated.

At 5000 feet the glider emerged from the cloud. Where was I? The land beneath me looked strange, unfamiliar. I panicked, force-landed in a field by the A31, seven miles away, and telephoned.

"You stay where you are, you .... Go back to the glider." The voice was tense with anger.

This was not quite how I imagined my first cross-country. One cow, two cows ambled towards me. I got out my mouth organ and played but the noise did nothing to discourage the sacred animals. They were about to start eating the navy blue fabric of the helpless Skylark.

"Is there anybody there, please, please."

The farmer came. The instructors came.

Grounded.

Up again, and determined not to make another mistake. This time my sin was a "beat-up". Losing too much height coming in to land, I went hard down to get up speed and gather enough energy to land inside the airfield. This was the right thing to do, wasn't it? It wasn't.

Grounded.

And ultimate shame, thrown out of the Kent and Surrey Gliding Club for lack of discipline.

In my bunk the army blanket seemed to weigh heavily on my body and the unexpected dishonour weighed heavily on my mind. No club would accept me now, however proficient a pilot I was. I'd only be able to use the Gliding Centre planes and that would be so restricting that any real progress would be impossible.

How was I fitting into this society, this country? What chance was there of becoming an instructor when everything here suddenly seemed so alien. What did these English people really think of me - a figure of fun, an oddity?

"Come and meet the Duke of Edinburgh," Ann Welch had said.

It was National Gliding Championship week and I'd been too busy at the winch to shave for several days. I was wearing someone's torn World War II jacket because of the cold and a filthy flying suit and boots.

"You are the only Commonwealth representative on this airfield. I've got permission. Come on."

"But I've already met him."

"When? Come on. Please, please."

The Duke of Edinburgh had made the royal helicopter divert to Lasham because he wanted a flight with Derek Piggott. Now here he was relaxing in the tatty clubhouse sipping coffee. He'd been given the chipped saucer.

"How do you do, sir. I did meet you."

"Where?"

"Durgapur, the Steel Project."

"Oh yes, yes. I remember. How do you happen to be here?"

"Well I just wanted to come on my scooter - you know - and learn to fly and now I'm subsidising my flights by being a winch driver... Can I get back to my winch now?"

"Of course you'd better get back."

No, there was no use pretending I wasn't different. Was that why it had all gone wrong?

Even Derek stopped talking to me after my disgrace. Nobody at Lasham seemed to understand me. At night I dreamt I was back in the great Ganges at Benares, drowning.

In the morning, the good flights, in skies alive with little cumulus clouds, soared around in my mind to taunt me. Would I ever be given another chance? It wasn't the qualifications themselves that bothered me, I explained to Daphne on one of our walks. But how could I live with myself if I didn't become an instructor, if I couldn't pass this privilege on, if I couldn't help others to discover the sky, to pivot round up there in utter peace?

Meanwhile I was still a winch driver and there was work to do.

One hot July day not long after my disgrace, stripped to the waist and wearing only rolled up khaki trousers, I was helping my boss, Bob, experiment with launches from a tow car. We were standing by the car at the launch point discussing technical details, our eyes turned towards the sky, a blue sky where Derek was performing aerobatics with a would-be instructor.

I tried not to think too hard about my own predicament as the Bocian went into a glorious loop at 1500 feet, about two miles to the north west of Lasham.

Upside down, still upside down, carrying out perfect turns. But something was wrong.

During the loop, the canopy had become detached, slid past and hit the tail, knocking the elevator out and making the glider uncontrollable.

The first little orange cigar on its parachute flicked out of the plane. The student instructor had bailed out. Then nothing.

"Come on Derek, bail out, damn you."

The seconds stretched for ever, then at last, only five or six hundred feet above the ground, we saw him flick out and disappear behind the hanger.

"Come on, Bob. Let's get in the car."

I drove the tow car at breakneck speed the one and a half miles from the launch point, across the road and up to the woods. Derek was hanging from a branch at the top of a tall tree, caught by his parachute.

"What are you waiting for? Get that rope to him."

"How the hell am I going to get down?"

"Don't you worry about that." I pulled the knife from my back pocket, seized it in my front teeth and shinned 30 feet up the tree, barefoot, as if I were climbing the mango tree in Danapur - Kalu would have been proud of my speed.

Derek was still swinging from a branch. "Keep swinging," I ordered.

Meanwhile the glider waffled along like a falling leaf and landed on the live wires, taking out all the power in the nearby village. Sparks flew and smoke began to wander into the hot air. Interested cows started to eat the fabric on the edge of the wood, while on the far side the once would-be instructor was able to step down to safety via a post. He never flew again.

Up the tree, I caught hold of Derek from behind, held him against my chest and cut all the nylon shrouds with my knife.

For a brief moment Derek broke his silence. "Toon, what have you done? You've ruined that parachute. It cost £25."

The silence resumed. But shortly after Derek's rescue and 15 days after my disgrace, I was checked out and allowed to fly solo again, back to the trainer T21B. Bliss.

In spite of the limitations of this glider, I was determined to learn all I could, to go up whenever possible. I hung around if there was any chance of a flight. The atmosphere of disapproval made me nervous, and very careful. But not careful enough. My second "beat-up" was the last straw.

Losing too much height again, coming in to land, I dived above the line of trees - and nearly hit them.

Grounded. This time it seemed for good.

August. The sun shone and Lasham was alive. I winched during the warm days and at night cried bitter tears into the dirty old pillow someone had given me. Not to be able to fly was agony. Nobody, but nobody understood me. How had I ever thought my dreams would come true when Dada handed me those rolled notes? How had I ever thought I would fit in here?

"Why don't you go and see Ted Shepherd - he has lived in India, perhaps he will understand. Don't get so upset, things will work out."

I took my friend's advice straight away. Ted was in charge of the Army Club and used to talk to me with a good imitation of an Indian accent. I cooked curries for him and his wife. They were both at the launch point. I knelt down quickly in front of Ted and got hold of his legs.

"Please help me. Please, please help me. I've got a real problem. Nobody understands me. Please get me back to gliding."

"What are you doing? Get off my knees. Come on, get up, get up. I'll talk to you later. Come and see me in the Army Club office after we've finished gliding."

I went to see him at five o'clock.

"Look, Toon, what are you going to do? Most people in Lasham absolutely love you but you do some horrible things. You'll smash a glider soon if you carry on like this. There's nothing wrong with your flying, but you keep breaking the rules. What can I do for you?"

"I don't want to fly high-performance gliders. I'll fly anything."

"Right. Let me have a think. Yes, you are going to fly the tea-tray."

"God bless you." Lord Shiva had heard my prayers.

The Tutor, nicknamed the tea-tray, was known as the slowest, most ugly-looking glider on the airfield. To me she was the loveliest thing with two wings.

The open cockpit resembled a tea-tray. With huge struts and high wings, the Tutor was designed to stay up but not to travel far. She was the slowest glider with the most drag - like a bullock cart with wings. There was no going any distance in her.

But she could soar at 30 mph comfortably and her stalling speed was only 24 mph. The turning circle was so small I could soar like a corkscrew in the middle of a thermal, going up, up, up, happiness bubbling inside me. The high-performance gliders with their slowest speed of 40-45 mph, could only turn in large sedate circles round the outside of us. But they could glide out of sight, cross-country, whereas we had to come down to earth again almost immediately.

I may not have had the best glider but I still had the best instructors. I was progressing again in my own way, and that was all there was to hope for then.

Towards the end of the summer it was hot, very hot - shorts weather, or dhoti weather if you happened to be an Indian. A dhoti or loin cloth involves six yards of material, cunningly applied.

My tea-tray was being launched by winch. At about 500 feet - whoosh - I realized with horror that my loin cloth had been sucked out of the open cockpit. It was fluttering behind me by almost the whole six yards.

I gathered my wits - first get out of sight of the ladies. I released and landed well up the grass area as though I'd had a cable break. But three ladies came to retrieve me.

"Stop, stop." I held up my hand to halt the feminine advance and lost any ground I'd made with the dhoti. I was all thumbs now. The ladies realized my predicament and started to giggle. It was suddenly as hot as Calcutta before the monsoon.

My blushes had hardly subsided before the story was being relayed with glee all over Lasham and beyond.

Sometimes, though, the dhoti stood me in good stead. In the summer extra staff were needed to help Cookie and that year a new manager, John, was appointed - a kindly, quiet man with five children. One of these children had a birthday.

"What about this birthday party? I've seen you amusing the children round here with your tricks ..."

Dhoti, *punjabi* and sandals made me look the part. The children loved the story of Manku, how I brought him up and lost him again, and the tricks he learnt. Then I tried a bit of yoga - standing on my head and trying to drink orange juice. It didn't quite work out but they didn't seem to mind. They clapped.

Then I showed them some of the balancing tricks from my circus days at Danapur, bottle on nose. More claps. The bicycle trick, standing on the handle bars. Claps again.

The tea-tray and I continued together into September. Nothing else mattered except flying, not even eating properly. My body eventually rebelled, I became very run down and nearly got pneumonia.

"If this poor Indian carries on like this, he'll probably die. He must be moved out of the bunk house."

Late September. The airfield was invaded with mushrooms, deliciously edible, but the nights were cold. I was moved from the bunk house to a caravan, a caravan so tiny that the bed took up the entire space, and it was still very cold. This was my home from then on. It was very near the kitchen so if the cold became too much, there was still the bench in the fireplace of the club bar and Min's warm fur.

The illness subsided, but now that I'd weathered my disgrace, the frustration returned. The wonderful tea-tray had saved me, but she was not going to take me anywhere. I was getting no nearer my goal like this.

"I must do something to start getting qualified," I fretted to Daphne as we trudged round Chawton, home of her favourite Jane Austen.

A solution came to me. I'd read enviously about Wasserkuppe in West Germany and the huge rounded slopes of the Rhön mountains.

The first summer camp there for gliding enthusiasts to fly together for fun and to build new gliders had taken place in 1920. Many of the pilots at Lasham flew there and came back enthusing. It was a kind of Mecca, a pilgrimage for any glider pilot.

I had accumulated three weeks' holiday and I was going there too. I was going to soar to my heart's content, I was going to achieve, I would have all the time in the world.

October. Wasserkuppe was blanketed in fog and rain for the entire three weeks of my stay.

On the last day the weather cleared to reveal what a beautiful place it was, surrounded by postcard mountains and fir trees and valleys. There would have been soaring in any direction.

I returned to Lasham dispirited. Even if the problems of time and money were overcome, how would I ever be able to achieve Silver C? Without this qualification there would be no question of becoming an instructor.

"Look, Toon, your talent is not for teaching people. Your talent is for cooking curry. You taught my wife and she's most grateful. I mean this - I will buy you a nice little restaurant where you can cook curry and put into practice all your ideas - one room Indian style where people can take off their shoes, have a wash and sit cross legged, and a more conventional room for other customers. It'll make pots of money which we'll share and then you can buy your own aeroplane like me..."

I looked after four Austers for Frank, Chief Engineer of Dan Air Maintenance and a keen glider pilot. This was in exchange for four hours' free power flying lessons every two months. It wasn't the first time he'd mentioned a curry restaurant.

"I'll think about it, Frank."

There was nothing to think about. It wasn't just a job that I wanted. It was a mission and a personal quest. Why didn't they understand?

November. The sky always leaden grey, the sun set lower and lower on the horizon and the evenings cold and damp, especially in the midget caravan.

"Do you not see how your Lord lengthens the shadows? Had it been his will he could have made them constant but he makes the sun their guide. Little by little he shortens them. It is he who has made the night a mantle for you and sleep a rest. He makes each day a resurrection."

I stared vacantly at the caravan ceiling, the filthy army blankets inadequate against the cold, while these fantastic holy sayings ran unbidden through my mind. There was still a candle burning in my heart, and a poster in the clubhouse fanned the flame.

St Auban in the Basses Alpes in France - applications for scholarships invited from pilots wanting to achieve their diamond heights. An advanced soaring school for three weeks in December 1961 - next month! I began to walk tall at the very thought of it.

But the two requirements I didn't have were Silver C and basic knowledge of French. Nothing to be done about the Silver C, but French? I got on the phone to Daphne. Her French was perfect. Would I stand the slightest chance of getting in?

CHAPTER 28

St Auban station was crowded with fur coats. My armoury
against the bitter cold consisted of two sweaters, my old winch
driver's jacket and a pair of trousers. And the sore throat which
had threatened since the last of my frenzied launches at Lasham
- my 299th - had blossomed into a full-blown English cold.

On the minibus, trying to stem the constant flow from
my big nose, I felt the first twinge of misgiving. The other
pilots who jumped aboard, dressed in smart coats and all
sporting Silver C and Gold C badges, chatted confidently in
French. My little duffle bag looked very scruffy next to their
smart *bagages*. Better concentrate on the view. We followed
a wide valley, then crossed a little bridge which led through
the village of St Auban. Right at the edge of the village two
or three hangars and a huge grass airfield provided the
backdrop for tremendous activity. Other students were
arriving in cars.

My excitement was tinged with a sense of unease. Did they
realize I hadn't a single leg of any gliding award? They certainly
didn't know that the letter, beautifully composed in French,
had been Daphne's doing. Still they were merely concerned
now with formalities - log book, passport ...

An Indian national! The secretary threw up his hands in
horror. The Chief Instructor was summoned, and then his
assistant, and they all threw up their hands and jiggled their
shoulders and spoke across me in rapid, agitated French.

They had thought I was a British national with a British
passport. This course was run by the French government
mainly for the benefit of the French armed services, with any
free places allotted to British, Italian, German, Dutch or Spanish
pilots. Not Indians.

What should they do with me? I'd arrived anyway, it was
their mistake and I had a rotten cold. So they put me through
the medical with the rest of the students.

They couldn't get rid of me on health grounds - my heart
was pretty sound. The Chief Instructor decided that I should

be taken up and down in a towplane to get rid of my cold - on the basis that pressure drops with a rapid gain of height, and body pressure drops too, automatically forcing the mucus out. A kill or cure treatment.

They shoved a towel towards me - by this time they'd discovered I didn't speak French, as well as having no gliding qualifications - and led me out to the Storch towplane.

We climbed straight up to 6000 feet and down again in three minutes. My head was banging away and I soaked their towel with no problem in only half a dozen trips. My heart was thudding too, with excitement at the view, the beautiful slopes above Mallefougasse, the Durance river... At the end of the day my lungs were clean and empty, and my head was empty too.

Back in the room to which I'd been assigned with the "other" British national, aptly named Mr English, sleep came easily. If, as I suspected, the drastic cold treatment had doubled as a kind of endurance test, I'd given the instructors no fresh grounds to get rid of me.

Next morning we were lectured on the use of parachutes, oxygen mask and other flying equipment. There were about 20 of us in the well-appointed classroom - quite a few French and Germans, two Italians, one Spaniard and Mr English who quickly became my interpreter. The use of radiotelephony was to be strictly in French so I made a list of the codes and memorized them, although there wasn't much hope of a solo flight for someone who shouldn't have been there in the first place.

Outside the temperature was -10°C, but I didn't feel the cold. The sky was cloudless, the sun shone and my spirits were high. It was obvious by now that this place was not just a playground for high and mighty pilots, but had a serious purpose. However much flying or gliding experience a student had it didn't matter, the instructors treated everyone the same. If only I could be allowed to stay.

Back in the classroom, everybody crowded round the board. There, with all the others, was my name. I never dreamt they'd let me fly at all that first day.

My turn came mid-afternoon. Monsieur Mandard had been allotted to me as the only instructor to speak reasonable English - or rather shout it at first as progress was very slow. What a privilege it was to fly with him in the streamlined Breguet 904 with its 20-metre wingspan, the most expensive glider of its class.

The other students were checked out quickly and sent off on their own in single-seaters - also pretty sophisticated but nowhere near the two-seater Breguet.

On my third flight with Monsieur Mandard we got airborne in quite turbulent conditions, with one of the highest aerotows of my life, 8000 feet - no winches here. Difficult to tell exactly what Monsieur Mandard thought of my flying, but he seemed happier as time went on.

On December 6th this pleasant routine vanished. *"L'onde!"* shouted the Frenchmen and everyone rushed out.

It was eight o'clock in the morning. The towplane, sent up first to find the wave lifts, looked no more than a tiny bee, way up high, against the beautiful clear sky in front of the Mallefougasse slopes. Everyone cheered.

"L'onde!" The wave. Here at last was the strong wave lift that made the site so perfect for achieving records. Excitement shot round the school like an electric current. Excitement tinged with fear - there was extreme turbulence with these conditions, and the terrible rotor cloud could form.

At eleven o'clock Monsieur Mandard beckoned to me. "Check the glider and get the oxygen masks ready. We'll be airborne in ten minutes."

God, I hadn't had this kind of experience. The rotor cloud lectures were vivid in my mind. It wasn't just the strength of the wind that surprised me now, it was the two windsocks on either side of the airfield blowing in different directions. I pulled my straps tightly.

As if the pictures on the classroom wall had come to life, parallel to the Mallefougasse slopes stretched a distinctive, scraggy cloud - a rotor cloud. This mysterious phenomenon, found only in this kind of mountain region, was formed, we'd been told, by violently unstable air.

Unstable? More like a gigantic tiger in the sky suddenly gone mad with fury, fur standing on end, attacking an unseen enemy, then slipping and rolling with its head down, turning a 360 degrees somersault but doing it so badly that at the bottom of the somersault its fur started vanishing, its body thinning out.

This furious tiger could be a mile long and here were our gliders, like tiny gulls, daring to fly within its range.

"What are you doing, Monsieur Ghosay? Come on. Wake up. Concentrate."

It was so turbulent, the plane was impossible to control. Monsieur Mandard took over.

"You haven't flown in rotor clouds? You don't know what you've missed. Look, don't go straight into the cloud because it's very, very violent. Stay on the upwind side so that you get the lift, then you are above it and in silence."

Tossed and plummeted round the sky, unable to see out, climbing to nearly 15,000 feet, oxygen masks on, fantastic turbulence. A lesson on how to fly rotor and wave, a matter of life and death, an unbelievably horrifying experience.

"I've never been sick before like this - please, please take over. I'm really ill."

"Oh you terrible man. What's the matter with you?" Monsieur Mandard took the controls.

No chance of being sent solo now. Not that I'd want to fly in anything like this again. Ever.

But the hell inside me gradually subsided. I tried to concentrate. Monsieur Mandard put me through all the exercises he could think of, showed me all he knew about the rotor. We were airborne for one hour and 19 minutes.

Thrown in at the deep end, now I was left to sort myself out. This reckless challenge of unpredictable elements was not merely about flying. A fragment of Dryden came into my mind:

"There is a pleasure sure
In being mad which none but madmen know."

Monsieur Mandard had been trying to show me how to be brutal like a tiger myself, pounce at the rotor cloud, and I'd actually been learning pretty fast. But how could you know whether you'd cope unless you experienced it yourself? I imagined the impossible, being sent off on my own into the cloud - OK, let's have it, you beast.

We all felt as if we'd lived through nearly two hundred years in one go. There was fearless Pedro, "but this is lunatic, *mon ami*" - he had regained consciousness at a mere 1000 feet above ground, Alberto the flash Italian with his heated flying suit and all the paraphernalia you could think of, and Jean Louis the Frenchman...

Another Frenchman, Paul, who'd also been up there on his own, stood apart from the rest of us and we watched him slowly disintegrate.

It wasn't as frightening for me as for the others - I had Monsieur Mandard. Apparently he was the only instructor who'd never had to bail out. Two instructors had been killed in past years and three had bailed out after their gliders broke up in rotor cloud. Monsieur Mandard wouldn't send me solo.

But it was still bad enough to give me nightmares.

That night I was flying an Olympia single-seater over Lasham, trying to stay up in the sky. Suddenly a violent upsurge tore the glider apart and I was out of control. Must bail out. I took off the straps but in my panic pressed the parachute harness loose too, ditched the canopy and stepped out. But my back was light. I'd got no parachute and I was going to drop to my death from 800 feet. I grabbed the side of the canopy with both hands, my body dangling over nothingness. I tried to lift myself up but all my strength seeped away. My grip loosened. Down, down ...

My screams woke the quiet Mr English at four o'clock in the darkness of a bitterly cold morning.

Oblivion again. The next thing I heard was Pedro knocking at the door, sent by Monsieur Mandard to see if I was OK. Yes, fine. I'd overslept.

Pedro tried to tell me about his flight in the rotor, waving his hand and foot to show how he had tried and tried to put the glider in a left-hand turn but how it was whipped to the right out of control and the turbulence was incredible - he'd experienced weightlessness in one moment and violent positive G, three or four times his normal weight, the next. Then black out.

A thrill of fear ran through me and I envied him the chance to survive that alone.

CHAPTER 29

There was enough snow to write "St Auban" on the back of one of the cars, the sun was out and a gentle breeze blew from the south-west. A hill-soaring day with no sign of waves. Monsieur Mandard put me through my paces, had me sweating my guts out.

Next day the temperature in the morning was -10°C, the sky absolutely blue, the sun out and the windsocks on either end of the airfield hanging limply. Monsieur Mandard didn't let me catch my breath - 1000 foot tow, 1500 foot tow, 2000 foot tow, another 1500 foot tow, all in quick succession. Then a south-westerly breeze sprang up.

"Well off you go and see what you can do."

My chance at last, though not so overwhelming in these perfect conditions. I hadn't flown a Javelot WA20 before. It was a very lively little single-seater glider with a short wingspan, and it suited me fine. I managed to stay up for 18 minutes, with a bit of hill soaring. That was enough for the moment. Exhausted and happy I could look forward to more chances to venture out on my own.

For the next two days it snowed non-stop. I thought of Wassekuppe. Maybe this was it, there would be no more flying, at least no more wave soaring. Mr English had stayed here for 21 days once, without a hint of wave-soaring weather, he said.

On the 11th I didn't wake till past dawn and Mr English was already at his prayers. He knelt by the side of the bed in his white woollen socks, very clean and neat, still in pyjamas, with his elbows on the cover and his arms folded, muttering hymns.

What was so different about this morning? The turmoil inside me matched the stormy wind outside, battering at the window panes. The corridor seemed to sing with the sound of hundreds of shuffling feet, the whole place was alive and buzzing with activity. My tiredness instantly disappeared.

Breakfast passed in a haze of unreality. Then outside into the ferocious wind. The windsocks blew in different directions, the vanguard Storch towplane had soared to about 15,000 feet, a tiny grey speck in a big sky. How many pilots would gain their Diamond height today - if they could survive the rotor cloud which would surely form?

I yearned to be up there with them, frightening myself to death, fighting to survive. But was there any hope after just one solo flight in St Auban?

In the briefing room, my heart thudding, the notice board swam in front of my eyes. Then it cleared - and there was my name. Last of three pilots to go up in a Javelot.

Fifteen to 20 gliders were spread all over the airfield. Three or four Storch tow planes started giving tows one after the other. The gliders soared higher and higher until at least half a dozen of them were out of sight. On the frozen ground my three woollen jumpers, with my overalls on top, barely kept out the cold.

Within an hour Alberto broadcast that he'd reached 5000 metres, the first Diamond height. He hadn't met the rotor cloud at all - probably it was too early. The two windsocks still blew in different directions, so terrific was the force of the gusts.

And my God, it was increasing. The German pilot before me in the Javelot returned with a ghastly crack on one side of the canopy. The mechanics took it into the hangar to repair. Waiting was agony.

It was after three when I strapped myself firmly in. Two people helped me to get the oxygen mask ready and lock the barograph in the fuselage away from the cockpit, so that any height recorded would be above suspicion. Would I reach the Silver height?

Monsieur Mandard came rushing out and felt my chest. "Yes, you're not too bad." He looked at my clothes, felt my shoes and checked the number of socks I was wearing.

"Have you ever been so high, ever in your life? What kind of gloves are those?"

He snatched my woollen gloves from me and threw them aside. The howling wind whipped them both away and they were never seen again.

"You're crazy, you're crazy, Monsieur Ghosay. Haven't you got any warmer gloves than those?"

He grabbed Pedro who was standing by in a happy daze after completing his height.

"Oh yes, he can borrow mine."

Monsieur Mandard handed over the very thick fur-lined gloves.

"Don't forget every ten minutes you call me and don't forget to switch off the radio afterwards. Bonne chance. Good luck."

He shut the canopy over me and I was off. I pulled the plug to release myself from the tug plane at 2000 feet.

With no time to waste, I turned quickly, looking for some lift off the Mallefougasse slopes. And there, in front of me in all its splendid horror, was the tiger, the rotor cloud.

My heart pounded in my head. It was like sitting on the edge of a thousand ton steam locomotive. A continuous funnel of smoke - huge - shot upwards with lightning speed. I flew on the steepest bank possible, weightless one second and weighing a ton the next. Sheer terror drove everything from my head. Who was I? What was my name? My father's name? The names of my 14 generations of forefathers?

The wings were flexing, moving up and down through five feet at least. How could this glider possibly hold together any longer?

We were timeless, the glider and I. The furious rotor had pierced me through the heart.

Monsieur Mandard hadn't told me my heart would stop. "Hang on," he'd simply said. "Be brutal." Like a tiger.

He hadn't prepared me for such turbulence as this. It snuffed out the breath of the sky. Lord Shiva was surely having fun and games, Lord Shiva whose almighty hand could grab my puny glider, turn me into a speck of spirit.

The variometer was right off the top end of the scale, maximum lift, the altimeter winding - the glider would have to fall apart now.

But what was this? Heaven? No sensation of flying. The sky was smooth, serene and beautiful, all excitement gone, the rotor cloud beneath me, like a vanquished tiger. I felt divine.

No, not divine - I looked out of the right side of the cockpit, put my hands together and bowed down to Lord Shiva and his goddess Parvati. I saw them in the dazzling white-capped French Alps. Southern France was spread beneath me in all its beauty and I was anchored here, motionless, timeless, in complete freedom and serenity. Only a whisper of wind through the oxygen mask.

The glider and I were one. *Om Shanti, om Shivaium*, peace. There was no taste, smell, hate, love. I was nothing - all caste, all religion, all dignity lost. Yet I was everything. *Om Shanti.*

"St Auban starter to Hotel Fox. Over."

"Hotel Fox to starter. Over." Was that my voice? How had I managed to speak?

"Give your reading."

"Let me think." Beastly man, Monsieur Mandard.

"What you say?"

"Position N.W. 10 km. Mallefougasse, above S.E. France, A.S.I. 105 kph. Alt. 6800 m and is stuck. Vario: 1m positive." My speech was slow.

"What is stuck?"

"Altimeter won't read any higher."

"Don't worry. How are you feeling? Can you see Delhi?"

"Out." He'd gone at last.

Peaceful, unreal again. Sleepy now. Breathe deeply in the oxygen mask. As if in a dream, switch oxygen supply to emergency. Very cold, -33°C on the gauge. Hands, feet, jaws and nose freezing. Head dropping forward onto my chest, not belonging to me any more. "Open the dive-brakes," echoed a voice from deep inside me ...

Where was I? Enormous pain clamped the side of my throat and neck. My head throbbed. The glider gently spiralled down. Wake up. Close the air-brakes and pull out of the dive. Turn the glider into the wind.

Recovered. I tried not to think about what would have happened without the air-brakes to slow my descent. Altitude loss explained the pain.

Below me was Volonne, eight kilometres downwind of St Auban. Shouting into the radio was a pointless exercise - the batteries were flat. I hadn't switched off after Monsieur Mandard's call.

Fifteen minutes' flight later I started gaining height again, wave-soaring - enormous sink then enormous lift, but I wasn't gaining much ground. It was around five in the afternoon. The sun still shone brightly up above but down below St Auban village was already twinkling with lights. I tried to increase my speed.

With 4000 feet to spare above St Auban I gently spiralled down. It was pitch dark by then - the windsocks had long merged into the blackness - and the wind was really strong. But thank God - rows of cars had been lined up with their headlights trained on a strip of the airfield and an arrow pointed into wind.

I stopped within a few metres of landing and half collapsed, conscious of being carried inside, having my outer clothes removed, being laid on a table in the warmth, watching celebrations going on all round me, wine flowing, mouths opening in strangely feeble song. The Durgapur tiger padded across my mind, magnificent, eyes glinting, making me smile knowingly. I'd survived.

By about 8.30 pm I'd recovered enough to have French brandy pumped into me, but it didn't make the room any noisier. The temperature outside was -10°C. Inside there was only warmth and celebration.

And there was enough for me to celebrate. The barograph showed a height of 25,002 feet, which not only gave me a leg of the Silver C but exceeded the height needed for Gold C and Diamond C as well. It also gave me the unofficial Indian height record. Who cared if I was deaf?

Nothing would stop me now from achieving the other legs to qualify for Silver C - duration and distance. Then training as an instructor would be within my reach at last. Nothing must go wrong now.

They'd found a leak in the oxygen pipe which hadn't been noticed when the cracked canopy was repaired the day before, so my loss of consciousness was easily explained. The doctor checked my heart and passed me fit. My hearing would eventually return to normal, he thought.

"Don't you do that to me again," said Monsieur Mandard as I set off to achieve the duration leg. This was to be a flight of five hours minimum.

It was a fantastic day. I took my oxygen mask off at 10,000 feet to eat bananas. How different from the day before. I tried to sink but I couldn't help rising. I was probably one of the few pilots in the world to spend five hours above 10,000 feet in a glider, but there was no skill involved.

Distance, the last hurdle, had to wait a day or two. Aix-en-Provence was the destination chosen for me. I pointed my nose towards the south-west and soared to 22,000 feet. The hard runway at Aix-en-Provence did not seem to materialize and suddenly the sea was beneath me and the wind tearing me along. From so high up Aix had looked like a tiny village and I'd missed the airfield altogether.

I turned into wind and could hardly make headway. Then the glider lost height, down to 16,000 feet, and two French fighter aircraft shot past beneath me. My God, I realized, this must be in the Marseilles control zone and my wooden glider was not showing up on their radar.

"Fox Tango to Bravo Quebec," shouted Monsieur Mandard over the radio. "Where are you? What is your position?"

"My position is not good," my voice gabbled. "Now leave me alone." I switched off the radio.

Losing height at a phenomenal rate, panicking, I could see Aix-en-Provence but couldn't reach it. After 20 minutes I managed to land in a field three kilometres south-west of it, 89 kilometres from St Auban. The field wasn't empty.

"This man does not speak French, please help him," read the letter Monsieur Mandard had given me. But these gypsies couldn't read. The dirty children, the pregnant women, the bearded lady and the old man stared at me suspiciously. I ran my hand nervously over my chin and it occurred to me that I hadn't had time to shave for days and with my black dishevelled hair and torn overalls ...

The children started stamping on the glider. I shouted at them and they backed away, frightened. We stared at each other.

"Saw you come down." The boy was out of breath with running, spoke in broken English which I could faintly hear - and wore three seagulls on his jacket!

My worries were over now. He fetched his instructor who put me on the train back to St Auban. I hadn't to bother about the glider, he said, they'd come with a trailer to pick it up, they had contacts with St Auban.

So that was it. I'd be returning to Lasham with a Silver C.

CHAPTER 30

It was snowing softly when I left St Auban on the Paris train. The snow was still falling steadily from Paris to Calais - no problem hitching a lift in such conditions. The crossing to Dover was cold and dark. When the parcel train from London delivered me, late, to Basingstoke at 4 am it shouldn't have been any surprise that it was snowing there too.

On the long walk from Basingstoke to Lasham snow swirled at me out of the blackness, like perfect miniature leaves. I wondered what Taffy was doing and thought of my lucky leaf. Caught it - a big flake melted on my tongue. The tired feet that crunched on endlessly seemed to belong to somebody else, but it could freeze and freeze and nothing would extinguish the glow inside me.

Lasham was asleep, dark and silent, a silence I could feel through my deafness. There was nobody about.

The caravan looked even tinier and somehow lost. The control tower stairs were steeper than before, almost impossible to climb, but at the top turning her head lazily towards me sat Min, lovely warm fluffy Min. The ash in the fireplace was still warm. Blankets from the cupboard? Just enough strength, then collapse beside the cat. Ah.

"I dreamt about you Toon. I knew you'd be back." Cookie with her wide smile was the first to greet me when I woke.

I watched her lips to see what she was saying but hardly a sound came from her mouth. Still deaf then. Outside silent white flakes slid past the window.

"... Diamond Height, Unofficial Indian Height Record, completed Silver C." You could tell by their faces most of them didn't believe a word - that silly Indian telling stories again.

Soon everyone had to believe it. My log book had been returned from Paris, my achievements ratified and the barograph recording proof in black and white.

Suddenly an unexpected hero, my sins were forgiven and restrictions lifted. Now I shall be all right, I thought. A kind of calmness came over me, and lasted even when my hearing was back to normal two weeks later.

"I knew you could do it," said Daphne.

"Yes, you've got Silver C," said Derek Piggott. "And enough experience with different types of gliders. You can come on one of the instructors' courses. But you'll have to get a power flying licence soon. A gliding instructor has to be qualified as a tug pilot."

The nearest aerodrome where I could train for a Private Pilot's Licence was Fairoaks, ten miles north-east of Farnborough.

An instructor from Fairoaks visited Lasham one weekday to learn to glide. He came down to the winch and shook hands.

"Ah the jammy devil with the Silver C. You come to Fairoaks and I'll sort you out."

"What will it cost me?"

"I'll just deal with you. Normally you pay four guineas but I'll make it £3.15s."

"When can I come?"

Tiger Moth

On the first Saturday I arrived half an hour early - not bad for a journey involving seven miles on foot as well as the train. There weren't going to be any problems - I'd already had some lessons in the Auster at Lasham.

This plane was a Tiger Moth. I remembered that first Tiger Moth at Hazaribagh, flourishing the red handkerchief on its wing tip, and smiled to myself. I remembered my first ever lesson in one in Calcutta and looked round expecting Baba's angry eyes. For a second a shiver trickled down my spine.

"This engine has an inverted system."

I nodded, although I didn't know what that meant.

I was strapped into the back seat, slightly loosely on the shoulders.

"We'll go to about 6000 feet. I'll do the take off and landing - you've done enough landings in gliders - and for the first exercise I'll put you in a spin and see if you can recover correctly."

I'd done enough spins in gliders but the speed of rotation in this powered plane with its shorter wingspan was something else. We must have done about three turns already. My head was going round and round.

"Right, I have control." I recovered and pulled the plane out smoothly.

The instructor applied the right rudder, put it back in a spin. So quick. Spin, recover, spin recover, for ten minutes. Fantastic.

"Right, we'll keep it in a spin and I will recover." He kept it going round and round, about ten spins, recovered, stabilized.

Suddenly we were upside down. What the hell ...? How could I possibly stay in the plane? I was hanging by the straps, clinging on to the side of the cockpit, over an abyss, screaming, "Stop it, stop it. I'm falling out." My feet had come off the rudder pedals, my knees were on my chest, one of my gloves had flown away. I was terrified. The Brookwood cemetery waited 1000 feet below me. I didn't want to die.

The plane rolled out and landed. I didn't know where I was. I got out and couldn't stand straight.

"Come on you silly Indian."

I staggered to the washroom, filled the sink with cold water and put my head in. I now knew what you could do with an inverted system.

A Private Pilot's Licence cost £50 to complete. Money from the bar jar was paying for this.

Meanwhile there was the British Gliding Authority pre- exam test with Derek, the first step towards becoming an instructor.

"You give me the patter," he said. "I'm taking off for the first time. You introduce me to approach and landing."

He was the worst pupil ever. He was flying so out of balance on his final approach - nose pitching up and down, wings rolling - we were bound to crash. Was this to be the accident predicted in my horoscope? Was I to discover it was all true, so near my goal? Lord Shiva, please, no. Another plunge. Panic.

"*Kee karta, Sahib*? What are you doing?"

How could anyone fly so dangerously, even in pretence?

"*Ye thik nay hai toomb Budhoo.* You're doing it all wrong, you idiot."

Derek, once an airforce instructor in India, understood Hindustani, the language I'd automatically used for gliding since Delhi.

"Look, before you even think of taking the exam, you have to improve your patter - in English."

It wasn't going to be as easy as I thought. My halting "patter" bounced back off the walls of the tiny caravan, filling my restored ears, as I practised into the night.

At least I didn't need patter for power flying.

On my third or fourth lesson at Fairoaks the instructor said, "I'm off. You're on your own now."

"Where are you going? What are you doing? That was an awful landing."

We'd been practising circuits - taking off, completing one circuit, landing. On the last landing the plane had bounced like a tennis ball. "Where are you going?"

"Mind your own business," he said. "Off you go."

The plane was much lighter on my own, easier to handle. Climbing, descending, stalling, spinning, I played in the air. It was a pleasure after that to clock up the required three hours of solo flying.

"Right, Mr Ghose. We're going to do the test next weekend."

Wing Commander Arthur was a real gentleman, rather short and stocky, red-faced, looking younger than his 60 years. He handled a plane as though it were part of his body, the wings just an extension of his hands. He reminded me of how as a boy I'd spread out my arms to fly like the kites in Lucknow.

"I've been to India, you know," he said.

"Have you? When?"

"I was there in 1933. There was an earthquake in Northern India early in '34. I flew over the earthquake sites in a Dragon Rapide with the engineers and reporters and officials. I still have the photographs. I'll show you."

"That's amazing. I was there too."

"No! You must have been very young."

The flying was easy to master but the written examinations were impossible. I'd failed them twice already. If I didn't get 70 per cent, the pass mark, at the third attempt there would be no Private Pilot's Licence for a very long time to come. And without that no hope of becoming a gliding instructor. How could this one examination threaten my whole future?

The last two questions - what the hell did they mean?

Wing Commander Arthur came and stood by my side, glanced at the paper.

"Look, Mr Ghose, multiple choice - A, B or C. A is out of the question. We know that it is B or C. Which one?

"B?"

"Yes, you're nearly right."

"Oh - C."

Passed.

There was no problem with the flight test. A beautiful morning, clear blue sky. Stall, recovery, spin, recovery, forced landing, steep turns, three circuits.

Passed.

"I know you're going to go a long way. When you become an examiner always remember if you do a flight test and find the student very competent, quite relaxed and very safe, pass him but help him if he's slightly slow in written examinations."

I felt infinitesimally small in an enormous sky that was home, playground, school and temple. Let this sky be a little more familiar, I prayed, a little more mysterious each day. Let me breathe it, become part of it, know it is my destiny.

Destiny. I thought of my horoscope again, that ten-foot scroll of yellow paper locked in Ma's almirah back in Calcutta. It had been right about the flying - nothing could really stand in my way. And the accident? There was no point in thinking about that. Accidents were part of life. I'd survived one already.

But there'd been another prediction.

Already in early September the nights were closing in at Lasham. Daphne had come to stay with me and after an early dinner we were walking round the edge of the airfield, hand in hand. The night was so dark you could almost pluck the stars out of the sky.

It was also destiny that I should marry a girl from across *kala pani*, the black waters. I looked at Daphne, who'd always been there for me. It was too dark to see her blue-grey eyes. Would she actually agree to become my wife? My heart began to thump.

CHAPTER 31

I was in optimistic mood. I'd just been passed out to give joyrides - not to instruct but it was still a breakthrough. My first customer was a white-bearded gentleman with a lovely smile.

"I've always wanted to fly."

He really enjoyed himself and I felt so good. It was a beginning. I had only to persevere and believe in myself to become a real instructor, to help so many people discover the wonderful world in the sky. That night I dreamt of beautiful things - gods and clouds and mountains, wonderful places, holidays in Kashmir, white horses, and Daphne.

"Toon, what are you going to do about me?" she'd whispered on that dark night, breaking the silence between us.

I told her.

She wanted to be married in three weeks' time - she'd waited long enough. It sounded easy. But no. She summoned me up to London and kitted me out in borrowed jacket and trousers.

"You will have to ask my parents for my hand in marriage," she said.

"Do I absolutely have to?"

"Yes."

I mugged up on how to ask for her hand, slicked back my black hair and downed a whisky. My knees were shaking. Daphne wished me luck and sent me off.

Mrs Wall was alone. I faced her across an expensively furnished room. The recliner was a bad choice of seat - it would not keep still.

Who was this who had the effrontery to ask for the hand of her only child, the apple of her eye? She was livid.

"You've got nothing. You have no standing, no money, and you want to marry my daughter? How dare you?"

I sat up in the chair and listened to her ranting on. The unaccustomed whisky gave me courage. Suddenly I went berserk.

"I've never met such a rude lady. I'm not marrying you, but your daughter, Daphne. Goodbye."

Mrs Wall's mouth gaped open.

I went straight to the nearest pub and cried into my beer, and into the next and the next. A repentant Daphne interpreted my incoherent phone call and came to collect me.

She still didn't let me off an interview with her father. Mr Wall drove down to Lasham and found me in my filthy winch-driver's gear. Although an accountant by profession, there was nothing he liked more than working with his hands. He had a lovely smile and a completely bald head.

"Can you afford Daphne?"

"I'm marrying her and she's marrying me. Between us we'll manage. I'm training."

He never asked anything else.

Three weeks later, incredibly, Daphne was my wife and we were starting out on an English style honeymoon.

"Can we go somewhere that looks like Kashmir?" I'd asked.

"Yes, we'll go towards Snowdonia. It's like the foothills of the Himalayas."

On the first day north of Ludlow, Daphne's white Ford Popular somehow started nosing right up into the hills above Minton. I stopped the car to watch a glider soaring away so peacefully backwards and forwards on the ridge. The familiar whistling noise and two tiny heads become visible. "Ah!"

We moved off, and somehow the car found its way up to the ridge. Long Mynd Gliding Club.

"I see. What are we doing here? Because you did say there wouldn't be any gliding ..."

"No, no just watching."

But Daphne started laughing. "Look darling, don't worry. We've known each other for seven years. Let's go and stay the night. It looks quite nice."

We took a room in the Gliding Club. In the bar an enthusiastic young instructor, baby blue eyes in a tanned face, joined me in a last drink.

"Have you done any flying?" he asked.

"No. Could I have a flight before breakfast if the weather is OK?"

"Yes, sure. You even get it cheaper then."

"What do you do on your first flight?"

"... push the stick forward, nose goes down, speed increases, wind noise increases ..."

"Will I be able to have a little go?"

"Yes you're going to fly most of the time."

Eight o'clock in the morning in a beautiful clear blue sky. "Right, Toon, you've got control."

I pushed the stick hard over to the left and we started screaming down.

"No, no not like that. You're very ham-handed."

I flew perfectly, then played again.

"Are you sure you haven't flown before?"

"No. I'm enjoying this."

When we returned, Daphne was still asleep and some pilots were having breakfast.

"Hello Toon, how are you?"

The voice made me jump. I hadn't expected to see an instructor from Lasham.

"I heard you got married on the 26th. What are you doing here?"

"I'm having a trial lesson."

"You, a trial lesson!"

A pair of baby-blue eyes turned towards us, suspicion growing. The truth was revealed and the eyes flashed.

"You stupid old fool. You've got eight times more experience than I have. Awful man. Making fun of me..." His voice was drowned out by laughter.

The car managed to keep on the road towards Caernarfon after that. It never went anywhere else by itself until its return to the thatched cottage we'd rented near the Golden Pot.

For a few months trouble managed to avoid me. Then it returned with a vengeance.

"You start walking. Just go away ..." My heart sank. I was for it again. I held the receiver at arm's length, wincing at the force of the four-letter words. Another angry instructor beside himself, Derrick Goddard this time. How did I manage it? It really wasn't my fault. I was hurt.

It had been just before Christmas and very cold, with a porridgy English sunshine. I'd been clocking up my hours in power flying on a cross-country trip in Lasham's Auster towplane. My friend Mike, a gliding instructor, was navigating. We'd flown to Shoreham to pick up Mike's father, John, for Christmas. John hadn't flown before and he sat in the back, smiling away, with blood pouring down his face. "Wonderful flight, I love it."

When the plane was parked he'd walked into the wind-driven fan on the starboard wing and sliced the top of his head. It hadn't looked too bad then, but with the pressure drop as the plane climbed, the blood poured faster.

"Where are we now, Mike?" I wanted to get John to a doctor.

"Petersfield."

"We're nowhere near Petersfield."

The fuel gauge suddenly caught my eye. The left tank showed empty. The right tank showed nearly full. How could that be, with only one fuel cock opening up both tanks?

"Look Mike, the engine is going to stop in a minute. We have to have a good look round for somewhere to land."

Dark, sad, eyes seemed to peer in at me from every direction, closing in on me. Baba. The horoscope. The words had echoed in my mind ... But no, not yet.

"Thank God." An enormous grass airfield with hangars.

A man was washing his car behind one of the hangars, steam rising in the hazy sunshine. Without looking up he said, "I know what's happened to you, you've lost your way."

"Where are we?"

"Upavon."

"What!" Twenty five nautical miles west of Lasham and we were supposed to be back by twelve.

"Look, we've got a casualty with us. I think it's a stitching job."

"No problem. This is a military airfield. We have doctors on 24 hour call."

The problems would be coming from Lasham, in the shape of the very angry instructor who'd shouted down the phone. I wanted to find out what had gone wrong before he arrived.

An inspection cheered me up. The cock float was caught up in a chain so only one tank had been filled when we left Lasham. That hadn't been my fault. Another five minutes and the engine would have stopped. We'd still been way off course though.

"Sit at the back. I'll sort you out." Derrick's voice was very gruff.

In the cottage that night - on my own now as Daphne had a job in Manchester and couldn't very well commute - I lay back and stared at the ceiling. Fascinating images of rivers and railway lines and a monastery-like building spun round. I'd first seen them as we circled above Shoreham airfield waiting for some signal from the ground, looking for Mike's father. To the south was the sparkling English Channel. That's the last thing I remembered before morning.

A few days later the snow started and Lasham was transformed. Someone had left an Austin 7 in front of the kitchen and six of us had to lift it bodily and carry it onto the road. Then I enjoyed my first snowball fight.

Gradually the airfield became deserted and the roads impassable. Even Cookie couldn't get in. We were the only ones left at Lasham - Anne and David, research students from Southampton University, myself, and of course the faithful Min.

Anne's sturdy snowmen guarded the airfield. Then it started snowing seriously and we were cut off. We could have been anywhere - the Arctic, Antarctica. I bowed my head with awe at the works of the goddess Parvati. To the north the trees were a mass of icicles hanging down - the branches had disappeared. Cracking noises echoed in the padded silence. The runway was covered in three or four feet of snow. It was spectacular and beautiful.

For three days we were marooned. We talked and drank and dreamt about the future. Anne and David were designing a man-powered glider to cross the Channel. Would they win the competition? How much nearer to my goal was I really?

Even if I qualified I knew a job at Lasham would be out of the question. When I qualified, not if. I'd got this far ...

One night while the others slept, a blizzard raged outside, not the gentle confetti snow I'd seen for the first time from my Chalk Farm window. This snow lashed unpredictably, uncontrollably, with tiger pounces, isolating us from the outside world. Alone, cut off - the feeling was familiar.

The noise of an army helicopter broke the eerie silence. Min cocked an ear. The three of us ran like children to the door. Tinned fruit for the marooned! Just a routine call.

In any case the worst was over. They began to clear the roads, although they iced over again almost immediately. I could get to the cottage at last. The impossibility of riding a bike on ice had not occurred to me. It soon did. I left the bike by the side of the road and walked.

With the weight of snow a tree had fallen onto the cottage roof. No electricity, telephone wires down. It was back on the bench with Min.

The runway had to be cleared - Dan Air needed to get their planes in and out for servicing. Snow banks six or seven feet high, like grounded cumulus clouds, were created either side of the runway and of course it iced up again, turning into a skating rink. The road round the perimeter of the airfield was the same.

"Let's go and do some skiing, Toon."

I had a good sense of balance but I'd never skied. Someone pulled me across with ropes to give me the feel.

"This is fun. Let's go on a bit of a slope."

I hit a ditch covered in snow. It was the white horse bolting from under me all over again. This time my left ankle screamed.

At the end of January the bad beautiful winter abated enough for us to go up. A whole month without flying! Aerobatics in the Swallow were unforgettable. Loops and chandelles over a strange landscape, uniformly white, unrecognisable. Where was the airfield? Was I lost again? About to disgrace myself? But then I saw the red winch sticking up above the white. Beautiful winch.

A few days after the snow we had a day of sweltering heat. "God, it's so hot. Very unusual isn't it?" Derek was flying with me on a spinning exercise.

No, it was only what I'd come to expect. In India we had definite seasons and the weather didn't vary within them. We knew where we were - summer, monsoon, autumn - whereas here, you never knew where you were or what to expect.

March. I wouldn't see out another spring at Lasham, whatever the result of the exam.

They considered me ready to take the British Gliding Association examination now. This involved an oral test and three flights to show my ability to teach. Here was the chance at last to prove that I could do it.

The examiner thought my patter in English was still not good enough. I failed.

The first signs of spring passed me by. The sky looked forever drab and the fresh green grass was squashed unnoticed beneath my heavy feet.

"Get yourself a good profession and spend the weekends at Lasham," advised Frank. "There's no money in flying anyway. Look, it's so down market. You'll get less than a sweeper gets, sweeping the streets of London."

"You'll never make an instructor with your English and your attitude."

Was I to end up running Frank's curry house after all?

No, it couldn't end here. I only had to believe in myself and hold on to my dream.

Everything was not lost. As an Assistant Gliding Instructor - the Silver C and a recommendation from the Chief Flying Instructor were the only pre-requisites for this position - and a tug pilot, I could at least get a job flying, though not of course at Lasham.

I gave a week's notice as a winch driver. I'd asked around the other airfields, especially those nearer Daphne. The Yorkshire Gliding Club at Sutton Bank invited me up. I had a feeling I'd get the job. There was nothing now to keep me at Lasham.

One April morning someone gave me a lift to the station. I left quietly, with my battered case and mixed feelings. I was attached to the place and I'd learnt so much, met so many people, but I hadn't quite made it. I hugged Min for the last time and felt the warmth of her old, old body.

I remembered her when the control tower was on fire, looking out at the top, mewing, too old to jump. The fire was too bad to rescue her by the stairs so I'd got a ladder and climbed onto the sill. She knew me of course and let me carry her down. I remembered the popping later inside the tower as the heat of the fire shot corks out of the wine bottles.

Funny that those corks popping should echo in my mind as we left the airfield behind. A sort of celebration with no-one to raise a toast.

CHAPTER 32

"Oo-oo," he shouted. "Look, they're making love."

The deep, growling voice startled me. I'd forgotten he was beside me in the open cockpit. The beauty of the North Yorkshire moors in the late April sunshine held me in a trance.

"Right. I'll have to give you a flight. You do the take-off and I'll show you round," Chief Flying Instructor Henry Doktor had said after the interview.

I'd watched this short, energetic, gnome of a man and wondered how he could produce such a deep, commanding voice. Now we were gliding round Sutton Bank in a red T21B and he was chuckling loudly.

We'd taken off from the plateau of the airfield, almost 1000 feet high. The winch launch had given us a mere 500 feet before we released and began soaring along towards the moors. I'd stared fascinated as the valleys and little wooded hills unfolded.

"Look, there's Gormire Lake," he'd said and turned very steeply past a pool of water set among the woods. "Oo-oo. Look they're making love."

I watched with a mixture of embarrassment and relief. Surely I must have got the job.

The couple by the lake looked round, couldn't make out where the sound was coming from, suddenly got up and scuttled away into the woods.

We sailed back silently over a huge chalk horse carved on the steep bank up to the airfield plateau, skimmed the pink heather and landed.

And what a job I'd landed. I was to be in charge of gliding instruction under the supervision of this Polish eccentric - and act as a tug pilot, maintain the winch and cables, act as barman when required and keep the clubhouse clean, including the ladies' and gents' toilets. I would soon discover the other little duties such as scrambling 500 feet down the hillside to switch on the water pumps.

The Yorkshire Gliding Club was smaller and far less busy than Lasham and it seemed to be perched on top of the world, a little paradise - and a challenge with its geography and its erratic weather.

The post was resident, with free board and lodging.

"Your room," growled Henry.

The wooden, ex-army type hut was separated from the main building, on rough ground. The four or five small rooms each contained bunks and a chair. My room was eight by six - just enough space for the bunk with my sleeping bag and a chair for my clothes.

"Look, have a polythene sheet ready."

"Why?" His suggestion puzzled me.

"Just take my advice."

Two weeks and a clap of thunder later I saw why. The water came straight down through the roof. I got my polythene bag, cut a hole for my nose, and fell fast asleep. In the morning, the room was flooded.

"Henry would you like to come."

"What's up?"

"I've got problems with my room. It's got too much water in it and my feet are getting really freezing cold."

Henry handed me a saw. "Look, take this into the woods there, cut down some trees and mend the roof."

An inspection up the ladder showed me the roof had a canvas covering and wasn't dangerous. Why should I be responsible later on for rotten wood? The room didn't worry me then. Water wouldn't kill me. I'd stick to my polythene bag. Or if it was really bad I could take my things and sleep on the floor in the main building. I had to go there to wash in any case.

As the weeks passed by, it was obvious that the state of my room wouldn't be a problem. I was so exhausted by the time I closed the bar at midnight that I could have slept up a mango tree in the pouring rain.

On fine days in the summer flying would begin at nine in the morning and continue until nine at night. Then there was the cleaning and the winch and the pumps and the gnome-like figure of Henry, tireless himself, always popping up to bark new orders.

Time was passing in a frenzy. I had to make the most of this opportunity, learn all I could. But I was a married man now, with a baby on the way and Daphne lived 101 miles away in a flat in Altrincham. I bought another old Vespa scooter, Sabrina Mark III, from Manchester so that I could visit whenever I had a free weekend - and that was all I could do for the moment.

At Sutton Bank summer drew tourists in their hordes, following the paths through the dusky pink heather round the plateau of the airfield, marvelling at the beauty we saw every day.

They stood above the white horse, looking over the vale of York to the Pennines - the white horse that was our landmark from the sky, a kind of welcome mat to any lost pilot.

They walked east and pointed at the fields spread out below them like a toy farm. In one of those fields instructors could land if they were caught out and missed the top of the steep bank.

"Not for you," growled Henry.

I never missed, and I never queried that I had to try harder than others to prove myself.

The tourists wrapped scarves round their heads against the wind or, when showers were forecast, looked doubtfully at the fat cumulus nimbus clouds, clouds that promised us soaring in thermals.

Summer also brought students, ten at a time for a week's trial course, every week until October.

"What is wave lift?" asked dare-devil teacher Mary, on her third day.

We went up to 8000 feet. We could see almost to Darlington, an amazing sight. Normally I wouldn't have taken anyone with so little experience up that high. The wind was blowing fiercely and yet it was absolutely silent. Fantastic.

We were up for a long time. Complete cloud cover, no sensation of flight but we were flying at 60 knots and had to keep the nose well down in order not to climb. I looked behind. Three or four gliders were trying to come forward to the Sutton

Bank flying area but they were drifting backwards and just couldn't make it. Another glider, a mile to the right was keeping level with me. I got a bit below the cloud and managed to land. So did Henry.

Sometimes he stayed about 300 feet above cloud, so that the winch wire was visible, but not the glider. I wanted to perform the Indian rope trick too.

"Yes, you can do that, no problem."

"But how do you see the ground?"

"Do a rectangular circuit above the cloud, then descend into wind."

"I'll show you the Indian rope trick today," I said to my students.

I took one of them up with me and followed the instructions. We came out of the cloud and dived. We undershot. An ignominious landing in the heather by the white horse. Just as the familiar little figure of Henry Doktor sprang out of his car.

The students had to manage without me for a few days that first summer. I was given leave to be with Daphne for a very special event in August. Her suitcase was already packed.

"Wake up!"

Two nights running I got a digging in the ribs, hared downstairs, heart beating fast, got the car running, dashed back up ...

"No, the pain's gone. False alarm."

On the third night I just turned over. "Not again."

Daphne was moving around. My God, was that her breathing so heavily? I drove her to hospital fast, at 5.30 in the morning, under a clear sky.

Back at the flat, after three disturbed nights, sleep was wonderful. When I woke up I remembered the instructions Daphne had left me. Washing machine first.

"Toon, you're the father of a baby girl, born just after twelve." Daphne's neighbour, director of Coronation Street, boomed the real-life drama up the stairs and everything else was forgotten in the rush to get back to the hospital.

"Where's the baby?"

Daphne was beaming. "Don't worry, you'll see her on the way out."

"Come with me," said Sister Stephen.

There were 12 babies together in one room, all crying. No, not quite all. Sister Stephen picked up one baby who had such a serene face, old and wise-looking, wrinkled, reddish with a tinge of brown. The baby's name tag read "Miss Ghose". She looked straight at me. I reached out to her.

"You mustn't touch her," warned Sister gently.

My daughter and I continued to look at each other. She should be called Nandita, I thought, after the goddess of mountains who possesses such wisdom.

At home there was chaos. I'd been filling the washing machine when the news broke. Now the kitchen was one foot deep in water. God, what was Daphne going to say?

And I'd made a worse mess than I realized. Downstairs an artistic neighbour had redecorated his rooms and gone on holiday. No-one knew that water was seeping through until he returned and by then it was too late. All the wallpaper had peeled off and his efforts were ruined.

The interlude at Altrincham was short. Back at Sutton Bank we were very busy, always on the alert. Storms erupted suddenly.

I'd been drumming into my students for five days how to control a glider with its huge wingspan on the ground in a strong wind.

"Keep the wing tip down with your toes - the wing tip on the windward side."

We landed at the first signs of the storm and I turned my back to fetch the trolley. Something made me look round.

"Roger!" An almighty yell, then I kicked him clear as he started to walk underneath the wing. The T21B turned right over. The windward wing tip had been up and the wind had caught it. Roger would have been trapped and I would have been responsible.

There was no time to sit back and think, to break the circle that spun in my head - when would I ever have time at Sutton Bank to sit for the full BGA qualification again?

Without it, how could I get a full blown instructor's job? If I stayed how could I keep the family together?

A weekend visit. Would little Nandita be awake when I arrived? Would she smile at me? Huddersfield - not too far now, but the road was blurring and my eyelids were drooping. I'd have to rest for 20 minutes. I parked the scooter at the side of the road and lay down in a field in my flying suit and anorak and woolly hat.

God, it was so cold and dark! Where was I? Night had fallen and I'd slept in the field for four hours. I jumped back on Sabrina and rode hard, cursing.

I hadn't chosen the best time for my late arrival. That day Daphne had managed to shut herself out of our first floor flat while hanging up washing in the courtyard. Baby Nandita was still inside. Daphne became hysterical and called the fire brigade. The firemen had to break in through the large window at the front (the flats were arranged round a square, the backs overlooking the courtyard) and Daphne was up that ladder before anyone knew it. She wouldn't wait. I could just imagine the scene.

The precious time with my family passed all too quickly. Almost as soon as I'd arrived, it seemed, Nandita was watching solemnly as I waved goodbye. This was no way to live.

But there was no time to think.

Towards October the courses started thinning out and at last the pace slackened, although there were always individual customers to consider. Then suddenly it wasn't very busy at all. And that brought a new problem. What would they do with me during the winter when there was only the occasional flying and tugging?

I wasn't like Henry, who could turn his hand to anything on the site. It was the instant of flight and the needs of the person sitting next to me in the cockpit that I wanted to understand and master.

Normally someone in my position would be detailed to help repair gliders in the winter months - a cold job I hadn't been looking forward to.

Fortunately I had another skill, which didn't go unnoticed.

Students forgot about any food they'd brought when the spiciness of my cooking tickled their nostrils. Sometimes they trooped into the main building with me and my curries and made a party of it.

So I was designated kitchen porter - in other words chef - for the winter months, cooking English dishes as well as my repertoire of curries, rice and lentils.

But I was to be paid eight pounds a week, a drop of two pounds. The average wage then was something like £20 or £25. What business did I have flying with a family to support? It was crazy. We should all be together.

But I knew deep inside that I had to follow my dream, even with Nandita's dark eyes burning in my mind on cold winter nights.

Daphne with Nandita

CHAPTER 33

In no time at all, the winter of 1963 was over, Nandita was sitting up, all trace of red wrinkles long gone, and I was a gliding instructor again, at ten pounds a week.

Some days that summer were very hot with blue, blue skies. On one of these days I was called out to do some tugging for the Yorkshire Gliding Club at Wombleton, only about nine miles away from Sutton Bank, but 1000 feet lower, almost down at sea level. A gliding competition was taking place and the disused airfield had come to life, buzzing with pilots and gliders.

I was to launch some of the competitors in an Auster. It was so hot. Inside the plane, with its closed cockpit, the temperature would be even higher, unbearable. I adjusted my dhoti - at least I would be as cool as possible and there wasn't an open cockpit for the thing to unwind and flutter out behind me. No chance of making that mistake again. Oh, no.

Dressed like an Indian, I squatted on the grass like an Indian, peacefully smoking my cigarette, looking forward to the day's events.

"Where are you Toon?" called a familiar voice through the megaphone. "You're going to take Philip Wills on Number One. Skylark Four. Where are you?" Ann Welch was in charge.

"Where are you going? Where are you going, you madman? There's a competition on." A burly policeman barred my way.

I'd stubbed my cigarette out with my foot and was making for the Auster - or trying to.

"I know," I said. "I'm the pilot."

"Don't give me that. You - a pilot? You mad Indian."

The heat pressed round us as we stared at each other. Ann to the rescue. "Please let him go. He is the pilot," came her voice loud and clear.

The policeman was dumbfounded. "I'd never have believed it. My God. A pilot dressed like this? Oh, no. What's the world coming to? Off you go, off you go then. Sorry Sir."

Wombleton was not usually such a hive of activity, but it did boast a hangar for the Slingsby glider factory in Kirbymoorside. Wombleton was nearer to the factory and had runways which made assembly easier. Besides, the wind at Sutton Bank was often too strong for gliders such as the Dart.

I'd been sent over there before to tow test planes but the job Henry gave me back in April was different. Firstly it meant cancelling my visit home as this would have been my weekend off - and I saw little enough of my family as it was. Nandita was eight months old. Would she still be shuffling around on her bottom in that comical way of hers or had she learnt to crawl?

Secondly a cold blast was whistling through the clubhouse door, numbing my legs, and outside I could see the Sutton Bank windsock standing on its end. No-one ever flies a Tiger Moth in winds over 40 knots.

"In this wind?"

"That's your problem."

Henry was adamant. I had to fly in the Tiger Moth to Wombleton where the test pilot, Derrick Goddard from Lasham, would be waiting in the Dart, land, keep the engine running, then tow him up.

"I must have some ballast then." Impossible otherwise with such a light plane.

So dark-haired Josephine came as ballast.

I saw the flattened heather and the beer cans rolling about on the ground, and shrugged.

We landed at Wombleton and kept the engine running.

"Test pilot wants 5000 feet Toon," shouted the batman as he waved me off.

Still climbing. Beneath us stratus clouds were building up. Trying to keep the airfield with its triangle of runways in sight was becoming impossible. It had gone. I was really disorientated now. Conditions high up here were quite calm but I still needed lots of rudder to keep the Tiger Moth straight. Why? Was there something wrong with the plane?

Derrick in the Dart behind me was pointing wildly. Eventually I turned east - I'd actually been flying north without realizing. There was a strong easterly wind and I was flying cross controls to keep straight. Derrick pointed again to indicate a quarter turn. Even then the airfield was invisible. Although we were at 5000 feet already, Derrick was still on tow. Then as I looked round, he gave the thumbs up, waggled his wings and peeled off.

But where was the airfield? It was still invisible. Why do I need to go back there anyway, I thought. Suddenly there was Gormire Lake glinting beneath some puffy stratus clouds. Now I could find Sutton Bank, but I'd need help when we landed in this howling gale-force wind. Communication with Josephine in front of me was impossible.

I landed. We would have been safe if there'd been anyone around, but even Henry had gone home. The wind was so strong on the ground I knew I'd have to keep the engine running at 1600 or 1700 rpm at least and put the tail up otherwise the plane would be blown backwards and severely damaged.

At last by knocking and shouting I made Josephine understand that she was to get out and call for help. Finding no-one in the building, she dialled 999. A fire engine arrived.

We couldn't even get the Tiger Moth in the hangar. Henry came back and we tethered it down out of the wind, close to the buildings. The wind blew for almost 24 hours and I kept looking out at the fragile plane from the window of my hut, alone, wondering what would have happened if I hadn't taken my ballast along.

It was never lonely in my hut even when there were no students in the other rooms. I had a companion. One day another Henry had wandered into my room - and stayed. Henry the Drake.

This Henry had been produced by one of the members of Yorkshire Gliding Club who'd gone to live abroad. We got to know each other - I would feed him in the morning (bacon was his favourite breakfast) and he would follow me around.

One day he walked all the way to my winch but when he heard the noise he didn't like it at all. He set up a terrific quacking and had to be taken back by one of the members.

He was rather a baby and he never tried to fly. He grew up at the club, became everybody's pet. At weekends there were quite a few people staying in caravans but on weekdays I was glad of his company, especially when it rained. He was a good room-mate. And this Henry never shouted at me.

One summer weekend we both had such a shock.

"Take Henry up and throw him out of the glider," said the other Henry suddenly.

"What! I'm not going to do that. Henry has never flown in his life. Suppose he goes and kills himself."

"I know drakes better than you do. God has given him wings and he has to use them. He's getting lazy and fat."

"I can't. Why don't you do it?"

"Get as high as you can - give him a chance and throw him out."

"But -"

"Otherwise I'll sack you on the spot."

"I can't fly *and* chuck him out."

"That's your problem."

I grabbed one of my students.

It was quite a good hill-soaring day. A large crowd gathered to watch. We took Henry up in a little sack with his neck sticking out, quacking in terror.

"Henry, I'll be with you all the way," I said, with a very sad heart.

We soared as high as we could and then turned into wind. "Chuck him out now."

The noise! He squawked and squawked as if he was going to die of a heart attack, dropped like a stone for about one second and then started flying. I watched him all the way, a tiny speck flapping vigorously towards the crowd by the clubhouse. He landed back on the airfield, into wind. I shivered with relief.

For over a week he never came anywhere near me. And he never flew again. "Sorry, darling," I said over and over and then he started to trust me once more.

I was run down. And the long hours of flying on hard seats took their toll. At last a painful fistula was operated on. The relief was enormous.

But soon there was no time to think again, no time to doubt what I was doing. At the back of my mind all the ambitions crowded - I had to be a fully fledged instructor, I wanted to go on to advanced gliders, advanced aerobatics, I wanted to get to the stage where I could teach instructors to teach, I wanted to extend into the sky.

But then there was my family - I wanted to provide for them and I wanted us to live together.

The privilege of passing on the freedom of the sky dispelled any doubts about what I was doing. All my students would really fly. And some of them were exceptional people.

Ken belonged to a bomb disposal unit during the war. A bomb went off while he was defusing it, blasted out his face and wiped out both eyes. Somehow his face was grafted together again, a story was written about his recovery and the BBC had him reaching 100 miles an hour in an open car on the M1. He visited Sutton Bank for a couple of weeks every year.

When we were introduced, Ken shook hands, linked his arm through mine and said, "How nice to see you, Toon."

The shock of seeing his makeshift face with no eyes and hearing his extraordinary greeting silenced me for a second or two. I quickly recovered.

"Very nice to see you too, Ken. When are we going flying?"

"What? I won't be able to fly."

"Of course you will be able to fly. You're very sensitive, aren't you?"

"Look. Let's talk about some important things, talk about flying later on. They're doing something here, aren't they? Show me round."

"They're rebuilding the bar."

Ken felt all round the semi-circular bar. "Any tables?"

"No."

He didn't need a stick, knew the way round from just one feel. The kitchen was the same.

"I've heard you make nice curry," he said.

"Come over the weekend. You're welcome."

It wasn't until we'd become good friends that Ken said tentatively, "You were talking about flying. What do you want to do with me then?"

"Well, we're going to learn together, aren't we?"

"How are you going to do that?"

"Look, you went round that bar. I showed you only once. You know how a glider flies."

"Of course I know the theory of flight but I'm talking about my sight. How can I see?"

"You said to me "How nice to see you", and I was absolutely shocked and yet you were looking at me. And now I feel that you can see things. I'll talk to you and you'll be able to see."

"No, no that's impossible. Let's think of other ways."

"I'll hand over the controls and we'll do the effects of controls you can feel. For example, when I tell you to move the stick forward the wind noises will increase."

Ken thought for a second. "That's it. When shall we go?"

"We'll go up first thing tomorrow morning."

A gentle breeze was coming from the west. We'd chosen a beautiful morning. I let Ken have the controls, got him to trim and feel the balance of the glider.

"You've got an open cockpit - if there's too much air blowing on your left cheek you have too much right rudder, so apply left rudder to balance the aircraft so that the airflow is coming straight on to your face."

Ken got that idea very quickly. The only problem was to keep the wings level. "Centralize everything by the feel."

"If the wind is getting too much you must be going down, losing height, and you can feel it in your stomach."

He even soared a bit, by feeling the bumps.

"I've never enjoyed anything so much."

The leaves were beginning to fall, heralding my second winter-regime at Sutton Bank. I hadn't stopped cooking curries during the summer though. The landlords of Hesketh Inn, at the bottom of a steep hill near Gormire Lake, had become great friends. South African Rosalind was a ballet dancer and once a week there were special evenings at the inn when beautiful music was played while Rosalind danced on the bar - and I cooked curries.

Rosalind and David owned a small stone cottage nearby. It had no electricity but a generator had been installed.

"Why don't you bring your family?" they said and offered me the cottage for ten shillings a week.

Excited, I carefully calculated my outgoings. If I were to earn twelve pounds a week - and that would be without board and lodgings - I could afford to bring Daphne and Nandita to this beautiful place. I was due for a rise anyway. We could be together as a family at last. There'd be no more travelling. I'd learn as much as I could, somehow make time to take the BGA qualification again. Yes ... The rest would follow.

I found myself with Henry Doktor after breakfast outside the hangar just under the windsock - a golden October morning with a lovely breeze from the west and the heather in full bloom.

"Come on, Henry, how about giving me some more money? Just two pounds extra and I'll be able to bring my family and live here happily ever after."

"Money? Give you more money? Look at you, you can't repair gliders, you haven't got the BGA full category ..." He waved his hands expressively.

"I only want to keep my family together," I exploded. "Wretched money. I'll have so much money one day I won't know what to do with it - you wait. I'll have my own fleet of planes ..."

Everything that had been boiling up inside me suddenly broke free. Henry watched in silent amazement.

"I've had enough of being exploited. I'm going and I'll never ever come back to Sutton Bank until I've got all the ratings. You listen to me very carefully. I'm not going to go back on my word."

One or two people turned and looked in astonishment, then hurried on. Henry kept calm. I walked away.

I had a long walk, by the white horse, along the ridge. Then I got Sabrina out and rode furiously, anywhere.

"I'll show them, I of the Kshatriyas, the warrior caste. With Lord Shiva's help I'll vanquish them all."

The Bengal tiger crossed the path of my mind and stared into my eyes. The old scooter shuddered at my speed.

Still seething, I found myself down by the Gormire Lake. "People just don't understand," I hissed as I wrenched off my shoes and socks.

God! The water was freezing. My feet were numbed.

The shock brought me to my senses. Life wasn't so bad after all, was it? I'd got so far and I had a lovely little family. There'd be another baby in a few months. Perhaps a son this time?

I rode back quietly and disappeared into the kitchen to cook lentils and rice, then packed my bags.

CHAPTER 34

"I think they were two nice, well organized flights, weren't they, Toon?" Ann Welch was smiling.

The airfield at Lasham suddenly sparkled, beautiful, and I was back up in the sky, really high, over the moon. I had passed.

But I wasn't going to use the qualification yet. My month as part-time instructor at Lasham would be ending. Next month I'd be at Cranfield on a course for instructors in power flying.

Instructors in power flying could earn a little more than gliding instructors, I'd told Daphne after my parting with Sutton Bank. They could better support their families. She gave me all her savings, £600, to qualify.

Wing Commander Arthur's spirit hovered somewhere near - no qualification in flying would be wasted, he'd said. One day, I promised myself, I would return to Sutton Bank with all the qualifications possible under my belt, and who knows, the fleet of aeroplanes too. I would show them.

Meanwhile Cranfield, the aeronautical college in Bedfordshire, was waiting for me. The Flight Instructor Course was starting on 3rd December, 1964. Cranfield was a complete contrast to the little paradise of Sutton Bank. It was on flat ground and more extensive than Lasham. There were three concrete runways and two very large hangars on the west side where experimental research work was carried out.

The accommodation was very cold but comfortable - no need for polythene bags against leaking ceilings. There were excellent facilities and dinner was in Mitchell Hall, named after the designer of the Spitfire, the Spitfires that had so thrilled me in the Chowringhee during the war.

It felt odd for the first couple of hours sitting in the right hand seat of a dual controlled aeroplane, instead of the left where the pilot sits. The student would be seated on the left and I, as the instructor, would be on the right.

The problem was the patter again. Knowing inside out what to say as a gliding instructor didn't help when an engine was involved. Once again my less than perfect grasp of English worked against me. The course was taking longer than expected.

"I know what we'll do." The Chief Instructor's wife Pam, who also taught, gave me a tape recorder - big and clumsy as they were in those days - with recorded instructions. I listened and repeated over and over in my room until the words seemed to dance with a life of their own.

Lectures had a distinctive smell, very pleasant. Ron Campbell, the Chief Instructor, smoked a black and brown pipe.

In the air the pipe was in position under the brown curled up moustache all the time, even while he was talking. This was no problem as he spoke very clearly.

"When you're coming in to land and you're about to round out at the numbers on the runway tell your student to round out at the height of an Indian elephant, take the power off and fly parallel with the runway until the aeroplane begins to sink ..." For anyone else he rounded off at the height of a double decker bus.

"I've heard you're very good at aerobatics but you've never shown me," I said towards the end of the course.

We were flying at 800 feet. Normally aerobatics are performed at 3000 feet at least, for safety reasons, but Ron wasted no time.

"There's my tobacco pouch. Put it by the compass near the windscreen. I'm going to show you a barrel roll, taking a reference point on the nose, diving down 30 degrees to the right, gathering speed to 120 knots, pulling up 45 degrees, then rolling round the reference point."

My excitement mounted. I knew how to do aerobatics in gliders but barrel rolls weren't possible because of the enormous wing span. Upside down I felt the negative G - weightless, hanging on by the straps. The tobacco pouch floated up into the air and I caught hold of it. We came back upright.

"Give me that tobacco pouch. That was awful. We should have had positive G all the time."

He started doing barrel rolls one after the other and that pouch moved from side to side but never once floated. Even if we'd had no straps on we'd have been firmly glued to our seats.

At the top of the approach to land, he turned the fuel off and stopped the engine. We glided down.

"Ah, that's lovely," I said.

Ron looked up at me as we walked back to the clubhouse. "The trouble with you is that you never go green, do you?"

Things were going well. I'd passed the flying and the oral test quite comfortably and was preparing for the written. At home in Altrincham we had a tiny son, very brown, completely bald, with lovely eyes. I couldn't wait to spend some time with him.

I thought of him as I drank a few companionable beers in a nice pub on the campus with an old man who used to be in the army in India.

"Do you take snuff?" asked the old man.

"I'll have a go."

"The Indians taught me how to take snuff and I got used to it."

"OK."

He put some snuff on the back of my hand. "Put your nostrils over it and inhale."

The first few times, what a wonderful sensation. Then I sneezed and sneezed and sneezed and couldn't stop. I felt something go inside me. Agony.

Two ribs were cracked.

"We used to put people in plaster but we don't bother now," said the doctor. "Try not to cough."

But I had a bit of a cold and I couldn't stop coughing. Studying was impossible with the pain. I took about seven days to get over it, extending the course and all the expenses involved. I got my rating on 12th February, a month after the birth of my son.

My first job as a power flying instructor started a fortnight later, part-time in Liverpool for five weeks, supplemented by some gliding instruction at Lasham. Liverpool was near enough to live at home.

There were still patches of crackly ice on the grass when 18-month-old Nandita and I played in Altrincham Park. She'd been walking for some time when she could hold onto a finger but wouldn't chance it on her own.

"Come to me, darling."

At last she did it!

"Good girl!" I said, scooping her up and hugging her.

"Goo gel." She took a few more steps, then decided that was enough.

But I wasn't standing still. I was pulling all stops to find a permanent job. Two letters arrived, one from Thruxton asking to see my c.v. and one from Shoreham inviting me for interview.

Shoreham? Wasn't that where Mike's father had cut his head open on the fan? I remembered the airfield in a kaleidoscope of rivers, railways, monasteries and sparkling waves.

CHAPTER 35

"It's only an old banger," my friend had warned when I sold Sabrina Mark III in part-exchange for his Ford.

"Never mind. It's a car."

It took 36 hours to get from Altrincham to Shoreham, even with my friend John as personal engineer. Fuel and engine problems meant that we broke down enough times for John to show his skill - every 30 or 40 miles. And it was raining.

We spent the night on the bar benches at Lasham, but there was something missing - no fluffy Min to cuddle up to.

In the morning the weather cleared and playful wisps of cumulus clouds gathered in a blue sky. The car still lurched from one problem to the next. Would I get there on time? We should have left even earlier.

My interview with Roy Bouchier, Manager of Sussex Flying Training was for 5 pm, on 23rd March 1965. We arrived, in sunshine, with five minutes to spare. I went straight up to the bar to ask for him.

A stout, bald man with a white moustache and very powerful eyes sat on a stool drinking gin and French. Wing Commander George Lowdell, Chief Flying Instructor.

"Good evening, Sir. My name is Toon Ghose ..."

An interview, then a trial flight with Roy Bouchier the following day. There was no doubting my determination. Was this why I got the job over a dozen applicants?

I was to earn twelve pounds a week, the exact amount I'd asked for at Sutton Bank, plus five shillings an hour. And by the end of the summer Daphne and the children had joined me - my little family in our own house. I felt good.

In the air, as before, only my student and I existed. But this time even on the ground my job was solely concerned with flying - ground work, washing planes. That felt good too, although there was the occasional sneaking nostalgia for my chef's hat.

In early 1966 my Assistant Flying Instructor status was changed to Qualified Flying Instructor, which meant that I could decide on my own when to send my students off solo.

"Do you think Graham's ready to go?" I wasn't used to the responsibility.

"You send him when you think he's ready."

He was flying perfectly. The sun had already set but that wouldn't be a problem, it only took ten minutes to do a circuit. I would send him now.

"Are you sure, Toon?"

"Just fly the way you flew the last circuit, Graham. And if the landing doesn't work out first time - perhaps the wind has changed a bit - don't worry, go round and sort yourself out next time. But you must land on the main wheels. Remember on your own you will feel lighter, climb quicker and float longer before you land or touch down. Good luck."

Together at last

I beat a hasty retreat, forcing myself not to look back. Graham was the first student I'd sent solo - it wouldn't do to let him see how nervous I was. Positioning myself by the control tower, I clenched my shaking hands and watched the plane like a hawk.

He took off, climbed to 500 feet, turned at right angles to the left, climbed to 800 feet and levelled out, then left for the downwind leg parallel with the runway, left again on the final approach and he was lining up ready to land.

No good. He'll never land like that. He's going round again. Don't panic - he must be nervous too. Next time.

He went round again. I nearly lost sight of him on the downwind leg. Now ... but again he was in the wrong position. It was beginning to get dark. He had no lights. Graham, Graham, what's happening to you?

On the third attempted landing the nose nearly dived into the ground. A stabbing pain in my chest.

Then he recovered, took off round again. Relief. But it was getting dark - next time he was going to prang the aeroplane for sure.

The Air Traffic Controller sympathized, but what could he do to get him down with no radio? What could anyone do?

Desperate now, I watched Graham's plane come in for the fourth time. If only this was a nightmare and I could wake up.

He made a beautiful landing.

Students were not my only concern. Sometimes there were customers who needed checking out, to ensure that they were still fit to fly a particular plane.

"Your name is Toon I believe. How do you do? My name is Dick, Dick Emery."

I had just returned from a flight. "How do you do?" I said. "What do you do for a living then?"

"Oh, you know. All sorts. But you'll be giving me a check flight in a Cessna 172."

"Oh, am I scheduled to do that?"

"Yes you are, and how nice to meet you. I've heard about you." He looked at me thoughtfully for a moment, then, "Do you watch television?"

"Not much. I'm flying all the time, aren't I? Got to keep the family going."

"Very good idea to keep the family going. Aren't you lucky doing something you enjoy? I'm the same, you know. I enjoy doing what I do. Let's go and fly."

"OK. Do you use a checklist?"

"No, I've flown these aeroplanes quite a lot."

"OK. Can you use the radio, please. I don't like using the radio much."

My customer sat in the cockpit and said over the radio, in a convincing Indian accent, "This is Dick Emery speaking. I'm going to be checked out by a flying chapatti."

"Who are you then?"

"I'm not going to be telling this flying chapatti who I am."

A lot of giggling could be heard over the radio.

His flying was superb, but he didn't want to spin, hated spinning. "I'll fill this cockpit up with lots of rice and chapattis if you give me a spin."

"This guy's quite funny, you know," I said to Wing Commander Lowdell when the flight was over. "I don't understand all the English jokes but he imitated me more or less perfectly, a bit like Peter Sellers."

"He's a world famous comedian, Dick Emery. That's his Rolls you see - 5RE."

I looked at the maroon Rolls Royce with the soft top parked in the car park. "Oh, that's nice," I said.

Sometimes I was detailed to collect an aeroplane from abroad and fly it back. It took too long to get visas for such jobs, so I was told to get a British passport.

With my little family installed in our own semi-detached bungalow and my British passport in the desk, India seemed far away.

An ordinary sunny morning in July. My first flight over, I'd signed off, ready to debrief my student. Wing Commander Lowdell poked his head round the door.

"Toon would you like to come in after debrief."

"Yes, sir."

Something was up.

"Sit down, Toon. There's a telegram. Your father has passed away."

"What do you mean? Are you sure, sir?"

He couldn't have. We always knew from their horoscopes that Ma would die first. Baba was supposed to live until he was 75, not 66.

In the silence that followed I knew it was true. Baba was dead. I stood up, and everything inside me seemed to have disappeared.

Wing Commander Lowdell looked at my face. "You can have the rest of the day off."

I left the room, and the airfield, and started walking aimlessly north along the river bank. A boat with swan-white sails drifted past, excited children on board wearing pink hats. The tide was coming in - round the toll bridge there were lovely ripples. In the distance were the contours of the soft green Downs, re-assuring. I thought I would recover.

"Baba!"

The yell, the sudden thundering sound, must have come from me, but I could have sworn it was my father's voice.

The screaming and crying began.

Later the bad dreams began.

Later still, the accidents.

It had been raining hard but now it had cleared up. The cloud base was 600 feet, with a nice north-easterly wind, but Rob in the Bolkow Junior was nervous.

"Would you like to fly solo again after this check, Rob?"

"No, not in this wind."

"We'll do three or four circuits together then."

We did two circuits.

"What happened there?" asked Rob.

The familiar lead-covered dome, once used for training gunners in airfield defence, had all its windows blown out.

"It's gutted inside. Some crank tried to blow it up in the night. Set fire to the wing of one of the aircraft too."

"Why do people do such things?"

"They must be sick."

On the climb of the third circuit we did not seem to be getting enough power.

"Did you check the carburettor heat on the downward leg, Rob?"

"Yes, I did shout out all the checks but you were dozing away..."

The rpm gauge, instead of staying at 2500, started dropping. I was wide awake now. God, what's happened to the engine? A loud bang. "I've got control," I said quickly.

At 400 feet the plane screeched and juddered as though it was going to fall apart. The propeller and engine stopped dead. Nothing.

Beneath us was the dual carriageway under construction, deep in mud after the heavy rain. God, we couldn't land there.

Instinctively, I dived hard and gained speed. Well, it's a glider now, I said to myself. I'm on my own, no radio. 120 mph. I pulled up, did a wing-over to come back to the airfield - impossible to turn with so little height - and with the speed had enough energy to land crosswind, on the airfield.

Not a nice landing, but nothing broken. The fire-engine, called by the Air Traffic Controller who'd seen everything, wasn't needed.

I looked at Rob. He was completely white but had a winning smile. "We're still alive," he muttered. Later he was violently sick. He never flew again.

My hands and feet wouldn't stop shaking and my knees were knocking together. There'd been no thoughts, no fear when the engine cut out.

The fear came afterwards, and the bad dreams. God, how had I survived? Baba's eyes were still watching me. Was this a warning from him?

It was discovered sugar had been mixed with the oil in the engine, seizing it up. Another of the crank's tricks.

The second accident was in another Bolkow Junior.

"Right, John, what would you like to do?"

"Whatever you think. I've been solo two years ago in Cessnas. Never flown a Bolkow Junior." He was older than most of my students - in his early fifties - and wore thick glasses.

"You'll like this. Nice plane. Visibility is so much better. We'll go and do some stalls, then put you round the circuit. How about that?"

"Yes. Fine."

Fortunately as it turned out, we were using a grass runway. The Air Traffic Controller gave us left base join for the finals.

"Nice approach, but you're a bit too high."

No response.

"John, you're too high. Rounding out at the height of three or four Indian elephants instead of one."

"What?" His face was completely screwed up. I thought he was going to have an epileptic fit.

He was a strong man. He put the stick hard forward and to the left, froze on the controls. The left wing went down and the nose dived towards the ground.

I lashed out to seize the controls, accidentally hitting him hard across the face with my left arm. I recovered the plane.

The recovery was a fraction too late. The port undercarriage hit the ground really hard. I must surely have broken the nose wheel and the undercarriage wheel.

But the plane bounced back, up into the air. I opened up the power and the engine was fine.

This Bolkow was one of the first to have a radio. The Air Traffic Controller had put the alarm signal on.

"Fly across and let's have a look... I can't see anything wrong with your nosewheel."

Test pilot Pewee Judge, in a bright red prototype Beagle Pup, heard what was going on.

"Toon, fly towards the west at a steady 80 knots and I'll have a look. I'm coming in on the starboard side."

He flew in close formation.

"Starboard undercarriage fine, nosewheel fine. I'll look at the port side."

The red plane disappeared from sight so I had a chance to look at John. He was half unconscious, his head and shoulder slumped to the left and his glasses had flown away. He was a greenish-white colour, slightly frothing at the mouth.

"Toon, your port undercarriage is askew." Pewee Judge had come to the port side.

Askew? Askew? What does he mean by that?

"Say again."

"Look it's only English - your left main undercarriage is bent."

"Oh thank you. Is it very bad?"

The late afternoon sunshine was streaming in the port window.

"Well it's hanging down. It's nearly torn off."

The Air Traffic Controller heard all this. "I'll clear the runways."

"No, I'll come into wind. I'll cut the engine and shut the fuel off, so there'll be no chance of catching fire."

I came in fast and kept going on the right wheel, keeping the direction down the grass runway with the rudder. Then the plane slowed down and the port side started sinking and rolled to the left, three-quarters of the way round, nearly facing the direction of landing.

John recovered quite quickly but couldn't remember what had happened. I remembered clearly, and now I was safe the fear came.

On my third brush with death I was quite alone.

"Go and check this aeroplane out, please, Toon. We've put a new prop on."

The Bolknow Junior had to be put through its paces. It had to be tested right through the speed range from very slow to very fast to see if there was any vibration on the propeller. Then on straight and level flight with maximum rpm. Nice and smooth, no vibration.

A perfect day. It was at the time when farmers had started ploughing the top of the Downs and I could see a tractor below me now, on the high ground near the little huddle of trees known as Chanctonbury Ring. The sun shone and the cloud formations took my breath away.

I'll try a quick inverted flight, just for a couple of seconds, I thought.

My aerobatic skills were self-taught. Instead of rolling the plane over on its back, I decided to do it off the loop, not appreciating the loss of momentum at the top of a loop - hardly any speed. I stalled upside down.

The plane went into an inverted spin.   I started going round and round, hanging upside down by the loose straps, frozen on the controls, completely disorientated, less than 1000 feet from the ground and spinning towards it.

I didn't know how to recover.   OK, I thought, I've asked for it.   This time I'm going to die.

I took my hands and feet off the controls and prayed.   Lord Shiva, help me! Hanuman!

The minute I took the power off, the plane came out of the spin on its own.   The nose dived vertically down at an incredible speed.   My God, I'm going to hit the ground now whatever I do.   Brief images shot through my mind at the speed of lightning - Ma blowing into her conch shell, Baba glaring down at me, grandfather sitting up on his funeral pyre.   Did his spirit fly free?   Would I fly after death?

But I had to try to get out of this.   There was my own little family ... I pulled the stick back a bit and right in front of me were the whites of a farmer's eyes.   The terrified farmer, on the tractor, ducked his head.   The plane pulled up gently, into the brilliant blue, at the last second.

The huge ball of fire which the Air Traffic Controller was expecting to see from beyond the hills never appeared.   Nothing disturbed the beautiful day.   *"Om Shivaium.   Om Shivaium."*   Thank you, Lord Shiva.

Difficult to believe I was still alive. I felt very ill.

That night and the next my nightmares made all the bad dreams seem like cosy fairy tales.   Tractors with maddened eyes reared up at me, my planes - I seemed to be in several at once - all nose-dived towards the ground at impossible speeds, again and again.   I screamed out and Hanuman leapt across the Channel to rescue me.   But when he saw who I was he laughed and turned away and where he'd been the clouds turned black and squeezed the breath from me, and Baba's angry eyes were watching.

How had I survived?   How was I going to last in this game?   Was I paying for my disobedience?

CHAPTER 36

The next day up in the enormous sky, weaving in and out of frothy mountains of cumulus, Baba's eyes had lost their anger. They were calm, protective. "Be humble," they seemed to say. "Take care. Always anticipate danger."

So many times the big hand of Lord Shiva could have picked me up and dashed me to the ground. But it hadn't.

Horoscopes? Baba was dead when he should have been alive. I had just as much chance as the next person.

Meanwhile my student was flying perfectly, circuit after circuit. It was time for her first solo. I surprised her.

"Now?" Ann turned to face me, excited, nervous.

The adrenalin began to pump round me too, though I knew she would be fine.

"Just fly like last time, Ann. And if you can't land safely for any reason, don't worry, go round and sort yourself out for the next time. But you must land on the main wheels. Remember you will feel lighter, climb quicker and float longer."

I wished her luck and walked away quickly in the direction of the hangar. As usual I didn't look back, although I knew she wouldn't be shouting after me, "Toon, no, I can't go," like some of the others.

From the hangar I watched her take off, climb and turn, the familiar tingle of fear running through my body. She would be fine.

I remembered Graham, the first student I'd sent off solo, and smiled.

No need to watch Ann all the way. I wasn't even sure which plane was hers now. Behind me in the hangar, a small boy was fingering the Tiger Moth with reverence. As I smiled at him and remembered another small boy, my mind cleared and it was as if a weight was suddenly lifted from me.

Here I was alive and doing just what I set out to do - opening up the sky for people such as Ann, helping them to feel the vibrations of the soul and just for a brief time the pettiness of life below, sharing a hint of the freedom that could one day be ours.

Yet I was only at the beginning. The search for something higher, with all its struggles and triumphs, could continue for as long as I wanted it to.

I couldn't foresee all the qualifications yet to be gained, or the fleet of aeroplanes that would be mine - just as I'd boasted to Henry Doktor.

I couldn't foresee the number of times I'd cheat death again, or the hopes and the disappointments, the richness of life when everything material was lost, and the succession of students I could still inspire.

There was no hint of my work in the mountains of Nepal following just a little in Jurgen's footsteps after all, or the dreams that would still sustain me.

I knew then only that the gods were smiling.

The small boy left the hangar, trailing behind his father, looking back wistfully. I searched the sky for Ann's plane - she would be on the downwind leg now. Yes, there it was, a red and white Cessna.

She made a perfect landing, just as I knew she would. I waited in the airport ready to greet her and offer my congratulations. She danced towards me across the tarmac, her face transformed, the breeze catching her hair.

"My God, Toon, what have you done? Oh, I'll never forget this day."